THE MASSIVE MILLENNIUM QUIZ BOOK

1000 Questions for 1000 Years

TERRY DEARY   MARTIN BROWN

■SCHOLASTIC

To Jenny for the last .025 of the millennium.

Scholastic Children's Books,
Commonwealth House, 1-19 New Oxford Street
London WC1A 1NU, UK

A division of Scholastic Ltd
London ~ New York ~ Toronto ~ Sydney ~ Auckland
Mexico City ~ New Delhi ~ Hong Kong

Published in the UK by Scholastic Ltd, 1999

Text copyright © Terry Deary, 1999
Illustrations copyright © Martin Brown, 1994 – 1999

ISBN 0 439 01213 9

All rights reserved
Typeset by Rapid Reprographics Ltd
Printed by WSOY, Finland

2 4 6 8 10 9 7 5 3 1

Contents

Introduction

A thousand years of torture and torment and testing! Yes, that's what teachers have been doing to poor pupils. . .

Have you noticed how they always ask about dusty dates, lousy laws or sad statistics? They never ask really interesting questions about the peculiar people who populate the past, their batty behaviour and horrible habits. They never ask about the foul facts, so you never learn the terrible truth about our awful ancestors.

You can't amaze your mates with dry dates. . .

No! You need terrible truths to share and shock. . .

So pester your parents or puzzle your pals. But beware! There's a rotten risk that you may end up knowing more about the millennium than your history teacher!

The 1000s
The nasty Normans

This was the age of the vicious Vikings, who'd been in Britain for 200 years. It was also the age of the Norman invasion. After William the Conqueror's fearsome Frenchmen landed at Hastings in 1066, life was never the same again for the English. The nasty Normans nobbled the natives and built enormous castles.

Quick questions

1. The Danish Vikings had been invading England for centuries and some had settled – but they weren't popular. In 1002 the good folk of Oxford found a way to deal with the Danes who'd settled there. What way? (Clue: they liked to chop and change)

2. In 1004 the people of Norwich made a deal with the Vikings to stop the raids. What did they agree? (Clue: crime pays)

3. In 1006 King Ethelred of England was worried that his nobles were becoming too powerful. He had one noble, Aelfhelm of York, murdered. What did he do to make sure Aelfhelm's sons didn't rise up in revenge? (Clue: they didn't see the point)

4. By 1009 King Ethelred was desperate. He had paid fortunes to the Danes and they still raided and robbed England. What did he order his people to do? (Clue: oh my God!)

5. In 1010 a medical book of cures was printed, but not many people could read. They preferred old charms like 'Out little spear if you are in here.' What does that cure? (Clue: saves nine)

6. In 1014 Danish King Knut invaded Lincolnshire and took hostages. But when he was driven out by the English he didn't kill the hostages. What did he do? (Clue: a bit of this, a bit of that)

7. The Archbishop of Canterbury was captured by the Danes in 1012. He refused to pay a ransom so the drunken Danes pelted him with what? (Clue: they were feasting at the time)

8. Ethelred died in 1016 and councillors in Southampton elected Danish Knut king – while councillors in London elected English Edmund. Two kings for one kingdom? But Edmund came up with an easy solution. What? (Clue: dead easy in fact)

9. Knut became King of England in 1017. What did he do to the mother of his rival, Edmund? (Clue: knot a bad idea)

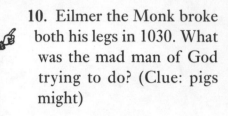

10. Eilmer the Monk broke both his legs in 1030. What was the mad man of God trying to do? (Clue: pigs might)

11. In 1040 Macbeth became King in Scotland. How did he kill the previous king, Duncan? (Clue: all's fair in love and. . .)

12. King Harthacnut accepted a drink from his half-brother and died in 1042. What sort of drink killed him? (Clue: half-brother gets the throne)

13. In 1054 King Macbeth of Scotland was beaten at the battle of Dunsinane. How long did he go on reigning after the defeat? (Clue: count Shakespeare's witches)

14. King Gruffudd of Wales was on the run from Earl Harold of Wessex. In 1063 he died but the English didn't get to kill him. Why not? (Clue: watch your back)

15. William the Conqueror landed at Hastings to fight Harold for the English throne. As he jumped ashore something went wrong. What? (Clue: clowns do it all the time)

16. After King Harold Godwinsson was hacked down at Hastings his mum offered Harold's weight in gold for the return of her son's body. Did William accept? (Clue: the answer is either 'yes' or 'no')

17. The towns between Hastings and London didn't have the nerve to stop the Normans. But the invaders still took a couple of months to make the short trip to London. What slowed the Norman army? (Clue: it took guts)

18. The Norman conquerors suffered several rebellions against their rule of England but the strangest one was from their wives back in Normandy. What did the women demand in 1068? (Clue: lonely)

19. In 1069 there was a serious revolt in the North where the Norman governor was murdered. How did William hit back? (Clue: smoking is bad for your health)

20. In 1071 the English were rebelling in Cambridgeshire led by Hereward. What sneaky trick did he use to discover the Norman plans? (Clue: Hereward Bond?)

21. King William fought with his oldest son, Robert. His second son, Richard, died in 1074. How did Dick die? (Clue: dangerous driving?)

22. Norman monasteries were schools for boys. Monk Anselm said, in 1076, that the monks were making the boys into beasts and he wanted to stop what? (Clue: beat it)

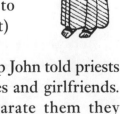

23. Norman Archbishop John told priests they couldn't have wives and girlfriends. When he tried to separate them they drove him away. How? (Clue: rock on!)

24. In 1077 the women of Bayeux made a memorial to William's victory at Hastings. It was 70 metres long but only half a metre high. What was it? (Clue: sew artistic)

25. In 1078 William ordered dozens of villages and churches in Hampshire to be destroyed to make way for a forest. Why did he want a huge forest? (Clue: not for firewood)

26. What was the punishment for a peasant who disturbed an animal in William's forest? (Clue: don't get a grip of yourself)

27. Abbot Thurstan was tough with his monks and they rebelled. Who did he turn to for help? (Clue: not the navy and not the air force)

28. In 1086 William ordered a report on all the English lands he owned – the Domesday Book. Yet he never read it. Why not? (Clue: lesson-less)

29. William was a tough man but as he lay dying he cried in terror. What was he afraid of? (Clue: the heat)

30. William died after a riding accident in 1087. The stone coffin was too small for his swollen corpse. What happened when the mourners tried to force it in? (Clue: pop!)

31. William the Conqueror died . . . and then killed two of his undertakers. Explain that if you can! (Clue: a load of rot)

32. William II took his dad's throne, though his Uncle Odo fought him for it. Odo never carried a sword or sharp weapon into battle. Why not? (Clue: bishops bash)

33. William II was proud of his yellow hair, but his enemies said the colour clashed with what? (Clue: enough to make Will blush)

34. Everyone remembers that in 1066 William I invaded Hastings from Normandy. But everyone forgets that in 1094 William II invaded Normandy from . . . where? (Clue: tit for tat)

35. The Pope called for a Crusade in 1095 and promised that any knight killed in battle for the Church would be rewarded. How? (Clue: gates will open)

36. The knights who succeeded in the Crusade got a different reward when they captured Jerusalem in 1099. What? (Clue: they cashed in)

37. Pope Urban II sent knights off on a Crusade but he never heard of their victory. What prevented his hearing the news? (Clue: sounds like deaf)

38. In 1096 William, Count of Eu, was punished for plotting against the king. The king had the ancient punishment carried out – even though most people thought it was too cruel. The count's private parts were chopped off and then what? (Clue: he couldn't cry about this)

39. In 1098 the Norman Earl of Shrewsbury fought the Welsh and ended up like Harold at Hastings 32 years earlier. What happened? (Clue: watch it!)

40. In 1098 William Rufus defeated and captured the Count of Maine (France). What did William do to him? (Clue: like a bouncer)

Name that Norseman

The people of the eleventh century were often named after their appearance. These nicknames were usually invented long after the person died by medieval writers. (It probably would have been a bad idea to go up to a Viking and call him 'Mr Flatnose'.) Can you spot the real names here?

41. Viking Chief, Thorkell the ...
a) Tall
b) Thin
c) Thick-as-Two-Short-Planks

42. Danish conqueror, Svein ...
a) Fork-tongue
b) Forkbeard
c) Fork-and-knife

43. Ethelred's son, Edmund ...
a) Ironheart
b) Ironside
c) Iron-me-shirt

44. Strathclyde king, Owen the ...
a) Bald
b) Hairy
c) Permed

45. Earl of Orkney, Sigurd the ...
a) Stout
b) Slim
c) Stuffed

46. Archbishop of York, Wulfstan the ...
a) Wolf
b) Fox
c) Yeti

47. Duke of Normandy, Robert the ...
a) Saint
b) Devil
c) Slightly Naughty

48. King Knut's son, Harold ...
a) Flatfoot
b) Harefoot
c) Five-foot-two

49. Norse king of the Irish, Sigtrygg ...
a) Silkbeard
b) Squarebeard
c) Bottle 'o Beard

50. Wife of King Harold, Edith ...
a) Swantail
b) Swan-neck
c) Swansbum

51. King of Norway, Magnus ...
a) Barefoot
b) Bareback
c) Bear-hug

Potty proverbs

The armies that invaded England brought with them terror, destruction, fear and . . . language! The Viking invaders brought many words that we still use today.

These incredibly intelligent words of wisdom would not be possible if it hadn't been for the kindly Viking conquerors. Can you spot the *three* Viking words in each of these little-known Norse proverbs?

52–54. A flat egg on the plate is worth two in the dirt.
55–57. Bulls without legs give fewer steaks to the butcher.
58–60. Grubby kids with freckles don't look so mucky as those with plain faces.
61–63. Thieves who crawl low are not seen from high windows.
64–66. Reindeer with scabs give rotten meat to stew at Saturday suppers.
67–69. Dirty fellows become dazzling when washed with soft soap.
70–72. A knife in the guts will get even the grandest to gasp.
73–75. A score of scowling scarecrows will scare scamps.
76–78. Those who die meekly will receive no glittering crown in heaven.
79–81. Walk awkwardly and cruel people will scream and call you lame.

11

Question of the century

82. William the Conqueror conquered English, he conquered Danes, he conquered Welsh and then he stopped. Why?

What happened next?

In history you can usually guess what happens next. But you may find it a little harder in Horrible History, because people don't always behave the way you would! Can *you* guess What Happened Next (WHN)?

83. Scottish King Malcolm II's invasion of England ended in defeat at Durham. The heads of the dead Scottish soldiers were cut off and put on display round the walls of Durham City. The relatives were upset, and some of the women of Durham felt sorry for them. WHN?

84. King Svein of Norway kept attacking England so King Ethelred of England paid him 36,000 pounds of silver to go away. Svein took the silver and used it wisely. WHN?

85. William the Conqueror was the son of a duke but his mother was the daughter of a humble tanner – someone who made leather from animal skins. Will's enemies used this to torment him. When Will besieged the town of Alencon in 1048 the defenders stretched animal skins over the walls. William took 34 prisoners and cut off their hands and feet. WHN?

86. William slipped as he jumped ashore at the head of the invasion of England. His men were horrified because they thought this was a bad sign. William's hands scrabbled at the stones on the beach. He rose to his feet and turned to his frightened men. WHN?

87. William was crowned just two months after he landed and defeated Harold at Hastings. He was a foreign ruler with a lot of enemies who'd rather see him dead than crowned, so guards circled Westminster Abbey to keep out trouble makers. As William was crowned there was a huge cheer from the congregation. WHN?

88. Earl Waltheof rebelled against the Normans and was sentenced to be executed at Winchester. He asked for time to say the Lord's prayer. He was so emotional he couldn't finish so the executioner lost his temper and knocked Waltheof's head off with one stroke. WHN?

AND NOW FOR THE SECOND VERSE

89. William's death was caused by a fire. He set fire to an enemy town, his horse stepped on a cinder, threw him and the fall burst his bladder. He died in agony. But his funeral was disturbed by another fire. As his coffin was carried through the streets a nearby house caught fire. WHN?

90. William II fought against his brothers Henry and Robert in 1090. The brothers captured one of Will's knights called Conan and took him up the stairs of their castle tower. Conan begged them for mercy but the brothers laughed. WHN?

91. William II's army sailed north to fight the Scots. They stopped off in Tynemouth for a break and rampaged through the town. They stole cloth from an old woman who put the curse of Saint Oswy on them. Next day the army set sail on a calm sea past the rocks off the coast of Tynemouth. WHN?

92. Robert of Rhuddlan rushed from his castle to stop Welsh raiders escaping in their ships. He was in such a hurry he went without his guards. He was easily captured and beheaded. WHN?

News of the World

What was happening in the rest of the world during the 11th century? Complete the missing headlines.

93. CHINESE PUBLISH RECIPE FOR ▮▮▮▮▮ (1043)

94. BYZANTINE EMPEROR TAKES BULGARIAN ARMY'S ▮▮▮▮▮ (1014)

95. ARCHBISHOPS OF MILAN AND RAVENNA EXCHANGE ▮▮▮▮▮ (1027)

96. FRENCH FEAR ▮▮▮▮▮ (1033)

97. ISLAMIC WARRIORS FORM GROUP OF ▮▮▮▮▮ (1092)

98. WORLD'S FIRST ▮▮▮▮▮ (1088)

99. KNIGHTS ON HORSEBACK FIGHT WITH ▮▮▮▮▮ (1065)

100. ROME FULL OF ▮▮▮▮▮ (1084)

Here are the missing words – if you really need them!

lances, punches, assassins, clocks, rotting bodies, eyes, gunpowder, end of the world

13

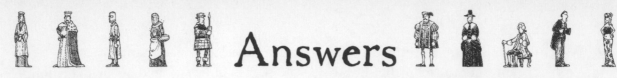

Answers

Quick questions

1. The Danish men, women and children in Oxford were massacred. The English chopped them to bits or fried them alive in a church like Danish bacon!

2. The people of Norwich paid 'peace money' – a bribe. Of course the Vikings took the money and then robbed and destroyed Norwich anyway! Wouldn't you?

3. Ethelred had them blinded. Nasty.

4. Pray. King Ethelred ordered everyone to go barefoot to church and eat nothing but bread, water and herbs for three days. He also ordered them to pay taxes or be punished.

5. A stitch.

6. He cut bits off them – noses, ears, fingers, hands and so on. Nothing too serious.

7. Cattle bones. He was probably stunned and didn't feel the killer blow – with an axe. Dane leader Thorkeld was disgusted by the murder. Even Vikings have feelings.

8. Edmund died. Knut became king of all England.

9. He married her.

10. Fly. He stood on a tower with wings strapped to his arms, waited for a strong gust of wind, then he jumped and flapped. He got 200 metres before he crashed.

11. In battle. Forget William Shakespeare's play where Macbeth stabs Duncan in his bed – Macbeth won fair and square.

12. A poisoned one. This murder was never proved but no one was bothered one way or the other. No one liked Harthacnut anyway.

13. Three years. Shakespeare got it wrong again! In his play (with three witches) Macbeth is killed at the battle of Dunsinane.

14. His Welsh friends killed him first. His head was cut off and presented to Harold as a prezzie . . . and it wasn't even Christmas! Harold then married Gruffudd's widow, Edith.

15. William slipped and fell flat on his face.

16. No. William refused to hand over King Harold's corpse, and had him buried on the shore.

17. Disease. When they reached Canterbury the Norman soldiers suffered attacks of dysentery (pains in the gut, diarrhoea and blood in the poo). Microscopic germs did what Harold failed to do!

18. 'Come home'. What they actually said was, 'Come home . . . or else!' And they threatened to find themselves some new blokes. The Norman lords who went home didn't get to keep the land they'd won in England.

19. He had every town and village burned to the ground. The crops were burned too and the cattle slaughtered, so even if the Northerners managed to hide they'd die of starvation.

20. Hereward became a spy. He disguised himself and walked into the Norman camps. It did him no good and he was defeated.

21. He fell off his horse.

22. Beating with a stick. The monk-teachers flogged the boys to make them work. But it's another 900 years before caning is banned in Brit schools.

23. They stoned him. He ran away as he didn't have a crash helmet handy.

24. A tapestry. With blue horses and green-haired men in places, it is a colourful picture of the Norman struggles.

25. For hunting. Only lords could hunt there, of course.

26. Having a hand lopped off. Peasants caught poaching were punished with a painful death or (if they were lucky) blinding.

27. The army. They broke into the church, massacred a few monks and splattered the blood of the others around.

28. William couldn't read.

29. Going to hell.

30. The swollen, rotting body burst open. Bits fell off. The smell was so awful the priests rushed through the funeral service and dashed off.

31. Two undertakers died of a fever. They caught it from the germs on William's rotting body.

32. Odo was a bishop and religious men weren't allowed to spill human blood. Instead they carried dirty great 'maces' that would crush a man's skull and kill him just as dead – but not spill blood.

33. His red face. His nickname was 'Rufus' which is Latin for 'red'. But would they have dared to call William 'Rufus' to his face?

34. Hastings. Of course.

35. They'll go straight to heaven.

36. Gold and silver. After murdering the

defenders the knights robbed the town and its temples. They fought for the Church – they robbed for themselves.

37. Pope Urban's death.

38. His eyes were put out. He was meant to live with his suffering but the torture killed him.

39. He got an arrow in the eye. It was an ace shot by King Magnus of Norway that did for the earl. Magnus said that he was aiming for the eye! In which case it's a bull's eye . . . sort of.

40. William grabbed the count and threw him out of the room. At least he let him live . . . very unusual for William!

Name that Norseman

41.a) 42.b) 43.b) 44.a) 45.a) 46.a) 47.b) 48.b) 49.a) 50.b) 51.a)

Please note: anyone who answered (c) for any question may need a brain implant.

Potty proverbs

52. Flat 53. Egg 54. Dirt 55. Bulls 56. Legs 57. Steaks 58. Kids 59. Freckles 60. Mucky 61. Crawl 62. Low 63. Windows 64. Reindeer 65. Scabs 66. Rotten 67. Dirty 68. Fellows 69. Dazzling 70. Knife 71. Get 72 . Gasp 73. Score 74. Scowling 75. Scare 76. Die 77. Meekly 78. Glittering 79. Awkwardly 80. Scream 81. Call

Question of the century

82. He ran out of conkers.

What happened next

83. The Durham women offered to wash and comb the hair of the dead heads so they looked nice and tidy.

84. Svein used the money to pay an even larger army, then he returned five years later to demand even more money. King Ethelred was forced to pay him 48,000 pounds in silver the second time.

85. He lobbed the hands and feet over the walls and said, 'That's what'll happen if you don't surrender!' They surrendered.

86. William looked at his hands full of stones, laughed and said, 'See! How easily I grab this land!' The joke relaxed his followers who went on to victory.

87. Everyone panicked. Guards outside thought William was being attacked inside so they set fire to nearby houses in revenge. The congregation heard the noise outside and many ran for their lives.

88. The head finished the prayer, saying, '. . .deliver us from evil. Amen.'

89. The coffin-bearers put the coffin down and went to help put the fire out. William was late for his own funeral.

90. They threw him out of the tower window to his death.

91. The ships ran aground on the rocks. Waves swelled up from the calm sea and swamped the ships, killing hundreds. The revenge of Saint Oswy?

92. The raiders sailed off – with Robert's head stuck on the top of the mast.

News of the World

93. Gunpowder. Printed in *Complete Compendium of Military Classics*.

94. Eyes. Emperor Basil had 15,000 enemy soldiers blinded and sent home, led by one lucky soldier in a hundred who was allowed to keep one eye.

95. Punches. The two holy men argued about who should have the honour of crowning the king of Germany.

96. End of the world. It was 1,000 years since Christ died and they thought the world would end on the anniversary.

97. Assassins. A group of ruthless killers whose duty was to murder people who opposed their religion.

98. Clocks. Described in a Chinese book, they were 10 metres tall and driven by a water wheel.

99. Lances. The spear was now held under the arm and knights could ride at each other in 'jousts'. The first tournaments were being held.

100. Rotting bodies. After the Normans destroyed it. But they had been invited there to defend the city!

The 1100s
Foul feudalism

This was the age of the feudal system, where kings were at the top of the heap and peasants at the bottom, with knights in between. Everyone knew their place and had to stick to it – not a bad life for a king, but a very, very hard one for a peasant.

Quick questions

1. King William II attacked a castle with a deep ditch. So that he could reach the castle, he filled the ditch with something rather disgusting. What? (Clue: neigh, don't do it!)

2. William II got the century off to a horrible historical start by getting killed in a hunting accident in 1100 – or was it murder? Huntsman Walter Tirel fired at a deer, missed and hit the king in the heart. What did he do next that looks suspicious? (Clue: channel hopper?)

3. William's corpse dripped blood all the way to Winchester Cathedral where he was buried under a tower. What happened to the tower seven years later? (Clue: t-rubble)

4. The new king was Henry I (who just happened to be hunting in the same forest when William was killed). In 1101 he met with his elder brother Robert. To show he wanted peace he gave Robert what? (Clue: 'x')

5. Bishop Flambard was locked in the Tower of London by King Henry but had a barrel of wine delivered to him. How did it help him escape? (Clue: wine was dopey and ropey)

6. In 1102 Archbishop Anselm got tough with Christians. He banned long hair for men but what about priests? (Clue: shorter back and sides)

7. Duke Robert turned against brother King Henry, so what did Henry do with him? (Clue: he held the key to his fate)

8. Archbishop Gerard died in 1108 but the churchmen refused to bury him in York Cathedral. That's because he was suspected of what? (Clue: did he own a pointy hat?)

9. A priest had been blinded and his hands and feet cut off in Norway. The Scottish King David took pity on him but he repayed the king's kindness by killing baby prince Malcolm with his false iron hands. How did King David punish the potty priest? (Clue: horse power)

10. In 1119 crusader Count Robert was captured and taken before the Atabeg of Damascus. The Atabeg drew his sword and cut off Robert's head. He threw the crusader's body to the dogs but what did he do with the skull? (Clue: bone china?)

11. In 1120 King Henry's son, William, was killed by a rock. How? (Clue: all at sea)

12. Rahere founded St Bartholomew's hospital, in 1123, after falling ill and seeing a vision of the saint (he said). Rahere gave up his job at the king's court. What did he do there? (Clue: funny sort of career)

13. The men who made the king's silver coins, the 'minters', were making a fortune for themselves. How? (Clue: tin men?)

14. In 1130 a Church law tried to ban knights from fighting for fun at fairs. What did it threaten knights with? (Clue: they'll have a devil of a hard time)

15. The Cistercian monks were known as white monks because they wore white woollen robes. Why white? (Clue: they don't want to die)

16. Jews became the country's money-lenders and bankers in the 1100s. For the safety of themselves and their money they built the first what? (Clue: they'll never be stony broke)

17. In 1135 King Henry I was killed by eels. How? (Clue: the eels died first)

18. Henry died and war broke out for his throne between his nephew Stephen and daughter Matilda. What horrible habit did Stephen have? (Clue: night nuisance)

19. In the war against Stephen, Matilda became trapped in the town of Devizes. They told her she'd never get out alive. Yet she escaped. How? (Clue: dead obvious really)

20. Matilda also found herself trapped in Oxford in the snow. How did she escape without being spotted? (Clue: the invisible woman)

21. Stephen was captured in battle in 1141 where he fought bravely with battle-axe and sword. But a soldier found a way to bring him down off his horse. What? (Clue: it's a knockout)

22. The Earl of Hereford was saved from death by his fine armour and great war horse even though he lost in battle at Winchester in 1141. How did he get home without being recognized? (Clue: chilly)

23. In a battle at Winchester King David of Scotland was captured three times. What did he do each time to get free? (Clue: follows the golden rule)

24. In 1140 the people of Lincoln went to a tournament, and the Earl of Chester attacked and captured the town while

they weren't looking! How many soldiers did he take with him? (Clue: a crowd)

25. In the Crusades the Christians used giant catapults and often fired flint rocks over the enemy's walls. Why flint? (Clue: a cracking idea)

26. Geoffrey of Bouillon sliced a Turk in two during a battle-charge in the Crusades. The top half lay on the ground panting. What did the bottom half do? (Clue: gee! Gee!)

27. The crusader Baldwin of France hid from Turkish enemies in a bed of reeds. The Turks didn't get their feet wet going after him. What did they do? (Clue: not environmentally friendly)

28. As Baldwin lay dying in Egypt he begged to be mummified and taken home for burial. His wish was granted. Which member of the army gutted Baldwin and preserved the body in salts and spices? (Clue: he served the army)

29. King Henry II's greatest enemies were his wife, Eleanor, and his sons. People said he protected his girlfriend, Rosamund, by hiding her where? (Clue: amazing)

30. Another story said Queen Eleanor found King Henry's girlfriend by attaching a thread to the heel of his boot and following him. What was Ellie said to have done with Rosamund when she found her? (Clue: invited her for a drink)

31. Henry's best friend was Thomas à Becket, but after he made him Archbishop of Canterbury they quickly fell out. Henry said he wanted rid of Becket and four knights decided to do him a favour. What did they do? (Clue: he axed for trouble)

32. In 1173 Queen Eleanor tried to escape from her husband's prison in disguise. Disguised as what? (Clue: she wasn't)

33. In 1189 Henry II died and his hated son, Richard, went to look at him in his coffin. What did the corpse's nose do to Richard? (Clue: left him red in the face)

34. In 1190 the Jews of York were trapped in the castle by a murderous mob. How did the men prevent the mob from massacring their wives and children? (Clue: DIY)

35. King Richard I (nickname 'the Lionheart') was a ruthless crusader. They said he kept enemy prisoners with his army. Why? (Clue: did he grill them?)

36. The monks of Glastonbury uncovered a skeleton in a hollow oak tree with a very handy lead cross that told them who it was: 'Here lies buried the famous King. . .' Who? (Clue: cutting corners on tables)

37. Richard I was shipwrecked travelling back from the Third Crusade and had to travel in disguise through enemy territory. He was supposed to be a kitchen servant.

What gave him away? (Clue: the finger of suspicion)

38. The huge ransom for Richard I meant terrible taxes for the English. A tax rebel William FitzOsborn was caught. What happened to him? (Clue: suspended sentence)

39. The century ended as it began with the King of England dying from an arrow wound – sort of. Richard I was shot in the neck during a siege in France. The shot didn't kill him immediately. What did he die from? (Clue: rotten business)

40. Richard died in 1199 and was buried. What unusual thing happened to the famous lion heart? (Clue: Richard lost heart)

Monk-y business

Could you have lived the life of a monk in the 1100s? If you think school rules are bad then could you stick to these rules? First, work out what they were by matching the right and left sides. . .

A monk will not. . .
41. think too much of his own
42. be tempted by
43. make a noise in the
44. argue with
45. be disorderly in
46. be careless in his
47. disobey
48. become as lazy as
49. want his own
50. think of the

a) senior monks
b) work
c) cloister
d) comfort
e) an old monk
f) world outside
g) brother monks
h) way
i) church
j) rich food

Question of the century
51. Where did young men go to learn how to fight?

Putrid poetry

Minstrels had to sing for their supper, but the songs that the knights enjoyed were enough to put most people OFF their food! Here is part of Bertrand de Born's cheerful pop classic. Can you fill in the missing gore?

My heart swells up with happiness every time I see
A mighty castle being attacked, its strong _____ (52) beaten down,
The _____ (53) on those broken walls being struck down to the ground,
While horses of the _____ (54) and fallen roam the field at random.
And, when battle starts to boil, let all you noble men
Put all your will to breaking _____ (55) and _____ (56).
I tell you that my greatest joy is just to hear the _____ (57),
'On! On!' from both sides and the _____ (58) of horses with no riders,
And the groans of, 'Help me! Help me!' from the fallen _____ (59),
And when I see the _____ (60) pierced clean through by shafts of _____ (61)!

If you need some help then here are the answers – in the wrong order.
wounded, spears, shouts, heads, soldiers, corpses, screams, arms, dead, walls

True lies

You know you can't believe everything you read. See if you can tell the facts from the fantasy. Simply answer true or false. . .

62. Wizo the Wizard lived in Wales in 1108.

63. The king's money was counted in the 'Exchequer' which got its name from the checked table that was used.

64. In 1114 Londoners walked across the Thames without a bridge.

65. King Henry I owned a gorilla.

66. The Normans killed lepers to stop them spreading their disease.

67. King Henry I's grave at Reading is now covered by a car park.

68. When King Stephen captured his enemy, Archbishop Roger of Salisbury, he locked him in the Tower of London.

69. Squires who were about to become knights were given a hot bath the night before.

70. In 1129 the Church tried to ban the crossbow because it was too cruel.

71. King Stephen took young William Marshall and shot him from a catapult because his father wouldn't surrender.

Medieval manners

How would you behave at a medieval dinner? Would you mind your manners? Or would you get a smack around the ear for your behaviour? Test yourself with these ten questions. Do or do not ...

72. clean your nails with your knife?

73. wipe your knife on the tablecloth?

74. play with the table cloth?

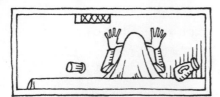

75. dip your bread in your soup?

76. blow on your soup?

77. clean your bowl by licking it out?

78. speak while your mouth is full?

79. spit over the table?

80. tear at meat with your teeth?

81. take the best food for yourself?

Knight school

There's more to being a knight than galloping about holding a joust, you know. You have to know how to *behave*. Would you have passed an exam in knighthood?

82. King Edward I of England has set up a 'tournament' (a bit like playing at having a real battle) and he will be fighting in it. What do you do?
a) fight in the tournament to the death, even if it means killing the King
b) fight with a special sword that won't harm anyone too much
c) refuse to fight

83. What is a 'knight errant'?
a) a knight who wanders round Europe looking for good causes to fight for
b) a knight who has failed in battle and is in disgrace
c) a knight whose favourite lady has turned him down

84. You are a knight captured in battle by a squire. This is a disgrace because he is not a knight. What do you do to the squire?
a) make him promise not to tell anyone
b) make him a knight
c) kill him

85. You get a message from a lady saying she is surprised to see that you still have one of your fingers. She thought you had lost the finger fighting in a tournament for her. What do you do?
a) send her a message saying she is mistaken
b) send her the finger
c) send her a finger made of gold and jewels

86. If a baby is to grow up to be a knight, how should his first mouthful of food be given to him?
a) from a silver spoon
b) from the tip of his father's sword
c) from the hand of a great knight

87. You agree with Ramon Lull's book that says knights should hunt bears, lions and. . .
a) rabbits
b) wild boar
c) dragons

88. You capture an opposing knight in battle. He is rich. What should you do?
a) kill him and steal anything valuable on his body
b) let him live and send him back to his rich family
c) let him live then sell him back to his family for a fortune

89. Some rather naughty priests had girlfriends. You agree with the suggestion that a woman who loved a priest should. . .
a) be given a good telling-off
b) be allowed to marry him
c) be burned to death

90 You meet a traitor in the cathedral at the coronation of your King Louis. What do you do?
a) kill him with your sword.
b) kill him by punching him in the head.
c) kill him after he's left the cathedral

91. Knights wore special colours and had crests on their helmets so that they could be recognized. What unusual crest did German Max Walther have?
a) a branch from a sycamore tree
b) a large parrot made from silver
c) a spike with three sausages stuck on it

The mad, bad, sad world

It wasn't only Britain that had a horrible history in the 1100s. Can you unscrabble the jumbled letters and find out what in the world was happening?

92. In 1152 the new Holy Roman Emperor was Frederick Barbarossa. His second name means 'Red _____'. D R A B E

93. Frederick Barbarossa refused to bow to the Pope at his coronation. In return the Pope refused to give Fred the _____ that would give him God's blessing. S K I S

I'M NOT GIVING HIM THE HOLY SNOW-SHOES EITHER

94. Barbarossa was upset when the city of Crema refused to surrender. He took the child prisoners and used giant catapults to lob their _____ over the city wall. D A S H E

95. Frederick eventually died when he was thrown from his horse as he crossed a river. In heavy armour he quickly _____ . W O N D R E D

96. William of Sicily didn't have a good reputation and earned the nickname William _____ . B A T H E D

97. In 1118 the Knights Templar were formed to protect the Crusaders and travellers to the holy city of Jerusalem. But the Templars weren't just soldiers, they were also _____ . S N O M K

98. The Emperor of Japan was forced to escape from his palace because of the war in his country. He disguised himself as a _____ . D A L Y – N I – W I N G A T I

99. Saint Bernard was a major monk in the early 1100s. He said, 'You don't just learn from books. You will learn more from the trees and the _____ .' S N O T E S

YOU ASK THE TREE, I'LL ASK THE SNOTE

100. Priest Arnold of Brescia told the world they should live poor and simple lives. The Church disagreed. He was arrested and _____ . E N D R U B

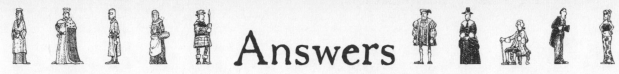

Answers

Quick questions

1. Dead horses. There was also a story that there were gaps between the horses so he filled the gaps with freshly slaughtered peasants!

2. Tirel fled to France. Would an innocent man do that?

3. It collapsed! The evil spirit of dead William got the blame.

4. A kiss.

5. The guards drank the wine and fell asleep. And there was a rope hidden in the bottom of the barrel that Flambard used to climb down his prison wall.

6. Priests had to shave their heads. King Henry had his cut and his lords all copied him . . . then trampled on the cut hair. Weird!

7. Locked him in prison – but only for 28 years!

8. Witchcraft and devil worship.

9. A horse was tied to each arm and leg of the priest then sent off in different directions. Ouch!

10. The Atabeg had it encrusted with jewels and used it as a drinking cup!

11. William's *White Ship* hit a rock as the drunken crew raced to overtake another ship. The *White Ship* capsized and all but two of the people on board drowned. No one had the nerve to tell King Henry that his son was dead.

12. Rahere was Henry's jester.

13. They took the silver out of the coins and replaced it with almost worthless tin. Ninety-four of them were caught and had their eyes put out. In Leicester forty-four more were hanged.

14. Knights who died in a tournament would go to hell. The Church would also refuse to bury them in holy ground. The tournaments were very popular and the Church law had little effect.

15. The Cistercians wanted to be as simple as possible. White is the natural colour of the wool (well, you don't see a lot of blue sheep) and dyeing it would be too fancy for them.

16. Stone houses. They didn't help much when the mobs turned against them and massacred them regularly in the Middle Ages.

17. Henry ate the eels and died. His doctor warned him not to eat them, because they usually made him ill – but he was a stubborn king!

18. Stephen snored very loudly.

19. Matilda pretended to be dead and was carried out in a coffin.

20. Matilda used camouflage and wore a white cloak to cross the snow-covered fields.

21. The soldier threw a stone and smacked Stephen on the head.

22. He dumped the armour and the horse and walked home. Of course knights wore very little under their armour so the Earl was almost naked – but it saved his life.

23. He paid his captors a ransom to set him free. This was a very expensive battle for David!

24. Three.

25. Flint shattered into sharp splinters when it landed and hurt far more people. One flint 'bomb' was said to have killed 12 defenders.

26. Rode off still astride the horse.

27. They set fire to the reeds. Baldwin was badly burned but still managed to escape.

28. The army cook.

29. In a maze. The story said only Henry knew the way to Rosamund in the centre. So how did she get fed? Or was she fed up enough with living alone in the middle of a maze?

30. Eleanor poisoned Rosamund – it was said.

31. The knights hacked Thomas to death at the cathedral altar. The top of his head was cut off and his brains spilled on to the floor.

32. A man. But the plan failed and she was caught.

33. Blood spurted from the corpse's nose and splattered Richard. 'The ghost is angry,' people muttered.

34. They killed their wives and children themselves. Many men then killed themselves. A few agreed to become Christians (as the mob demanded) and left the safety of the castle. They were butchered.

35. He was supposed to have kept them to eat if food was short.

36. Arthur. The find was a great attraction and the monastery became rich. Surely these holy men wouldn't fake this find . . . would they?

37. He wore an expensive gold ring. It was worth several years' wages to a kitchen servant. This seems like a stupid mistake for Richard to make – the story probably isn't true.

38. He was hanged. FitzOsborn was dragged naked through London behind a horse. Then he was hanged in chains so he died slowly as an example to the 50,000 rebels he tried to lead.

39. The doctor's efforts to dig out the tip of the arrow turned the wound poisonous.

40. His heart was buried separately. Richard's body was buried at Fontevrault, near his father . . . but his heart was buried at Rouen.

Monk-y business

41.d) 42.j) 43.c) 44.g) 45.i) 46.b) 47.a) 48.e) 49.h) 50.f)

Question of the century

51. They went to knight school, of course.

Putrid poetry

52. Walls 53. Soldiers 54. Dead 55. Heads 56. Arms 57. Shouts 58. Screams 59. Wounded 60. Corpses 61. Spears

True lies

62. False. Wizo did move to Wales in 1108 but he was the leader of a group of knights from Flanders, not a wizard. What did they call their best knight? Whacko?

63. True. The table was 3 by 1.5 metres and marked with black and white squares. Counters were moved around to make a simple calculator.

64. True. The tide was so low – and the river so full of mud and rubbish – that the water was only knee high and many walked across.

65. False. He had England's first zoo with lions leopards, camels and even an African porcupine – but he didn't have the thrill of a gorilla.

66. False. Henry's wife, Matilda, founded a hospital for lepers and many rich Normans left money to run leper hospitals too.

67. True. Henry founded Reading Abbey and was buried there. Now you can park over a king's bones.

68. False. He locked him in a cow shed (very smelly) and threatened to starve him to death if his castle didn't surrender.

69. False. They were given a cold bath.

70. True. The crossbow bolt would go clean through a knight's armour so a peasant could kill a lord. In war the lords were supposed to kill the peasants. The crossbow changed all that and this was clearly unfair and not very sporting – if you were a knight!

71. False. Stephen threatened to do this but felt sorry for the boy and let him live. Marshall went on to be a great English knight.

Medieval manners

72–81 All are DO NOTs.

Knight school

82.b) At Edward's tournament, the knights fought with whalebone swords.

83.a)

84.b) Many knights believed they should only be captured by another knight. It was simply a matter of a knight putting a hand on a man's shoulder and saying, 'I knight you.'

85.b) That's what nutty knight Ulrich von Liechtenstein did.

86.b) Dangerous but true.

87.a) Yes – fluffy little bunnies.

88.c) Ransoms were quite common by the end of the 1100s.

89.c) Priests were not allowed to marry. French knight-poet Guilhem suggested that any woman who falls for a priest should be burned to set an example to other women.

90.b) French knight Guillaume d'Orange killed traitor Erneis d'Orleans this way because it's all right to kill a traitor (even in church) but you should not spill blood on holy ground.

91.c)

The mad, bad, sad world

92. Beard
93. Kiss
94. Heads
95. Drowned
96. The Bad
97. Monks
98. Lady-in-waiting
99. Stones
100. Burned

The 1200s
Dark knights

This was when the Age of Chivalry really got going. Knights were bold, crowns were gold and ... er ... grannies were old. Life was cruel for kids and crueller for the weak, the old and the women.

Quick questions

1. King John took Richard's throne and in 1200 he took a wife, Isabella. He couldn't have married Isabella these days. Why not? (Clue: not a teenager)

2. In Scotland in 1222, the Earl of Orkney objected to paying taxes to the Bishop of Caithness. His men marched into the Bishop's house and captured his assistant, Serlo. What did the men do to Serlo to persuade the bishop to give in? (Clue: rearrange the letters of Serlo and you get 'loser' – which is the truth!)

3. The Earl of Orkney's men tortured the Bishop of Caithness with darts and stones. When this didn't work they tied him to his kitchen door-post and did what? (Clue: if you can't stand the heat)

4. The Scots king, William, was angry with the Earl of Orkney for the Bishop's murder – but couldn't get his hands on the man. What did he do to the 80 men who watched the murders? (Clue: foot loose but not fancy free)

5. William held the Earl of Orkney's son as a hostage. What did William do? (Clue: can't see how he can be blamed)

6. There was family trouble for King John when nephew Arthur went to war with him for French lands. John captured Arthur – who then disappeared. What do people say happened to Arthur? (Clue: he's in-Seine)

7. The Irish princes wore their national dress and long beards. What did King John do when he saw them? (Clue: it upset them)

8. In 1213 an English force set out to invade France. When they crossed the Channel they met the French sooner than they'd expected. How? (Clue: a quay victory)

9. John's leading army commander was half-brother William Longsword. After defeats in France, John got a similar, but mocking, nickname. What? (Clue: think he's hard enough?)

10. John demanded huge taxes to pay for his French defeats and the barons rebelled. In 1215 King John went to the Tower of London. Why? (Clue: it's not just a prison)

11. John gave in to the barons and set his seal on their Magna Carta – Great Charter – giving them power. But some rebel barons didn't turn up to watch. Why not? (Clue: they don't want to be headless chickens)

12. John was crossing the Wash sandbanks when the tide came in and caught his party. His life was saved but what did he lose? (Clue: it crowned a bad year for John)

13. John's accident in the Wash is famous. But what was he *doing* there, risking his life and his fortune? (Clue: he's *not* known as Lionheart)

14. John stuffed himself with peaches and cider to comfort himself for the loss of his jewels. But something even worse happened next. What? (Clue: bad die-t)

15. John had been wicked so he went to his grave dressed to look saintly. What did he wear? (Clue: he left behind his bad habits)

16. John was so hated by the religious people that after his funeral people reported a strange sound. What and where from? (Clue: deadly revolver)

17. There was also a story that John was a monster, not a man. What sort of monster? (Clue: anyone got a silver bullet?)

18. When John died his son, Henry III, was crowned with a bracelet. Why a bracelet? Two reasons. (Clue: king of the kids)

19. Henry III made Boniface the Archbishop of Canterbury but the chief monk objected. What did Boniface do? (Clue: must have been Boxing Day!)

20. Henry III's wife was very unpopular. As she sailed down the Thames the Londoners threw rubbish at her. What did she do? (Clue: she isn't having that)

21. What was Henry III's nickname? (Clue: Simon?)

22. In 1234 the Earl of Pembroke was wounded in battle. The best way to seal an open wound was to put a hot knife over it. The surgeon heated the knife. What happened next? (Clue: trust me, I'm a doctor!)

23. In 1244 Henry's daughter, Margaret, got engaged to the King of Scotland's son, Alexander. Margaret was a little older than Alexander, but how old was she? (Clue: she was a child of the 40s)

24. In 1251 the King of Poland sent Henry III a polar bear as a gift for the Tower of London zoo. The bear fed itself.

How? (Clue: something fishy about this)

25. In the middle of the 1200s a knight called Ulrich of Liechtenstein was riding round Europe fighting for the glory of his lady. What was odd about Ulrich's costume? (Clue: he was well dressed)

26. In the castles of the 1200s what did the gong farmer do? (Clue: did he have a clothes peg over his nose as he worked?)

27. Henry III's sister married Simon de Montfort and Simon invented the first parliament for barons to meet. They bullied Henry into signing a new sort of Magna Carta called the 'Provisions of _____' Where? (Clue: boat race)

28. Simon de Montfort was defeated when he fought the king's forces at Evesham in 1265. What gift was sent to Lady Mortimer after the battle? (Clue: something Simon lost)

29. In 1269 a peaceful monk called Roger Bacon makes something very un-peaceful. What? (Clue: the army take up the idea like a shot)

30. In 1270 two men played a chess game and made it extra difficult for themselves. How? (Clue: there were no pupils present)

31. In 1271 Simon de Montfort's sons took revenge for their father's death by murdering King Henry's nephew, and chopping him up. But they cheated.

They attacked him where? (Clue: he was altared)

32. In 1272 Henry III died while his son, Edward, was on crusade. Edward was stabbed by an assassin, but survived to become King of England. Why shouldn't he have lived? (Clue: not a clean cut case)

33. Edward's coronation was bad news for 60 pigs. Why? (Clue: couldn't save their bacon)

34. In 1286 Alexander III of Scotland fell off his horse. What was the horse doing at the time? (Clue: playing at being a seagull?)

35. Edward I of England decided to control Scotland. He began by destroying Berwick on the border. What order did he give about the corpses of the Berwick people? (Clue: it's a rotten idea)

36. Scottish kings were always crowned on the magical Stone of Scone. How did Edward I put an end to that? (Clue: Scone's gone)

37. Scot Braveheart, William Wallace, beat the English at Stirling in 1297. What did he threaten to do with the English leader's skin? (Clue: b_l_ up!)

38. The 1297 battle is known as the Battle of Stirling Bridge. What important part did the bridge play in the battle? (Clue: crossing it was a cracking idea)

39. Winner Wallace was never popular with the other Scottish lords. What was wrong with Wallace? (Clue: family problem)

40. Edward took revenge for Stirling Bridge the next year. For this he got a nickname, the _____ of the Scots. (Clue: Ed's as hard as nails?)

Question of the century

41. Where did King John sign the Magna Carta?

Castle cwiz

Could you survive in a 1200s castle? Match the left and right halves to see how deadly a defender you would make. . .

42. Protect your walls against fire using

43. Drive back your attackers with

44. Make powerful catapults from

45. The castle toilet was a good place to store

46. Attackers could reach your walls using

47. Attackers sheltered from your fire under

48. Attackers might shower you with

49. Lords moved from castle to castle with

50. Attackers had to beware of

51. Defend your walls from battering rams with

a) boiling water.

b) your best clothes.

c) secret trapdoors.

d) a tortoise.

e) furniture.

f) skins from dead animals.

g) bales of straw.

h) human heads.

i) a wooden tower on wheels.

j) human hair.

Odd one out

This is London in 1299, but some things are out of place – or rather out of time. Can you work out which things are right and which are wrong?

Knight rules OK

What do you think the rules were in a tournament? Tick the rules you would agree with if you were a knight in the 1200s. . .

68. No stabbing below the belt.
69. No biting or kicking.
70. No trying to kill another knight.

71. No running away.
72. No using cross-bows or arrows.
73. No attacking a knight in a 'safe area'.
74. No attacking a knight who's waving a white flag.
75. No falling off your horse.
76. No sneaking up behind a knight and attacking him.
77. No attacking a knight who is not in full armour.

Potty prizes

Tournaments offered prizes for the winners – and some of them were very strange indeed. Which of the following were actually given as prizes in tournaments? Answer true or false. . .

78. A bear.
79. A sack of coal.
80. A golden thorn.
81. A peasant.
82. A silver lion and a velvet cap.
83. A golden vulture.
84. A helmet with a silver dragon's head, two golden wings and lots of red, white and green feathers.

85. Leaves made of gold and silver.
86. A pair of talking parrots.
87. A copy of the Bayeaux tapestry.

Ropey relics

Relics were objects that had belonged to a saint . . . at least, that's what people *said* they were. Having a relic in your church or monastery attracted visitors, so it was a good idea to have a few lying around . . . like the head of John the Baptist, which the French cathedrals at Angers and Amiens *both* had!

Which of the following could you go and see in Europe in the 1200s? Answer true or false. . .

88. A piece of the Virgin Mary's robe.
89. Some of Saint Peter's hair.
90. A stuffed rabbit that had been on Noah's Ark.
91. The coals on which Saint Lawrence was roasted.
92. A piece of Saint Eustace's brain.
93. John the Baptist's finger.
94. A piece of the Virgin Mary's sandal.

95. A leg of the donkey on which Jesus rode into Jerusalem.
96. A piece of bread chewed by Jesus.
97. Part of Saint Radegonde's jawbone.
98. The crown of thorns placed on Jesus' head at his crucifixion.
99. The lips of Judas that had kissed and betrayed Jesus.
100. Saint Apollonia's teeth.

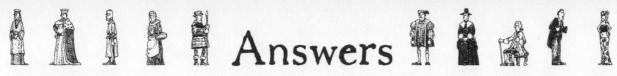

Answers

Quick questions

1. She was too young. Isabella was just twelve years old (although she'd already been engaged, to the Count of Lusignan). John's first wife had been divorced because he was too closely related to her – she was his cousin. He certainly picked odd brides.

2. The Earl's men murdered Serlo.

3. They set fire to the house and the result was a fried bish.

4. The king had their hands and feet cut off. Many died as a result.

5. William had the son blinded.

6. John murdered Arthur, they say. At dinner one night he became drunk and took Arthur to a bridge over the river Seine, murdered him and threw him into the water where a fisherman found the corpse. Arthur was just 16.

7. John laughed.

8. The English found the French fleet about to set off to invade England! The English destroyed the French ships, wrecking the French invasion plan, and then went home.

9. Softsword. And, because John lost so much of the land that Henry II had won, he got another nickname – lack-land.

10. John hid in the Tower for safety because it was his strongest fortress.

11. Some barons were too scared to attend. Rebelling against the king was a crime that could be punished by execution and if John got enough support he could tear up the Magna Carta then come after them.

12. He lost the crown jewels in the Wash.

13. Running away from a French invasion in the south.

14. John died. He had been sick with dysentery during his flight from London. The peaches and cider didn't exactly kill him but they did help to finish him off.

15. A monk's habit.

16. John turning in his grave! There was a rumour that monks dug him up and buried him outside the holy ground of the churchyard.

17. A werewolf.

18. The royal crown had been lost in the Wash, of course. And Henry was just 9 years old, so young a full-sized crown would be too large for him. He made do with one of his mother's bracelets.

19. Boniface went to the chief monk and thumped him. He then told his followers to beat up the monks.

20. She threw it back.

21. Simple.

22. The surgeon used the knife to murder the earl.

23. Margaret was just three years old. Alexander was three months younger.

24. The bear was put on a lead and allowed to fish in the river Thames.

25. Ulrich wore a dress and a wig so he looked like a woman. He promised a gold ring to anyone who could beat him – and ended up giving away over 250 rings.

26. He cleaned the toilets. The waste fell into pits below the castle walls. When the pits filled up the gong farmer shovelled it up and carted it away.

27. Oxford. Of course Henry broke the agreement just as his dad, John, had broken the Magna Carta.

28. Simon de Montfort's head was sent to Lady Mortimer who was very happy to receive it.

29. Gunpowder. The first in Britain.

30. They played blindfolded! Don't ask why.

31. He was killed in church. At least they were decent enough to drag him outside before they butchered him.

32. The knife was poisoned. But Edward I was a tough young man – as his enemies soon found out.

33. Sixty pigs were slaughtered for the coronation feast so the guests could pig out. There were also hundreds of swans and peacocks as well as 3,000 chickens.

34. Jumping off a cliff. Alexander died. But was it an accident? Or was the horse pushed? We'll never know.

35. Leave them to rot. The sickening smell would remind the Scots what had happened and that Edward was boss.

36. He pinched it and took it to England where it stayed for 700 years.

37. Turn it into a sword belt. It's said that he did

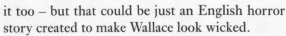

it too – but that could be just an English horror story created to make Wallace look wicked.

38. The bridge collapsed under the weight of English knights. With no bridge they were trapped on the Scottish side of the river; they couldn't escape back and help couldn't get forward so they were massacred.

39. Wallace didn't come from a great Scottish family. The great Scottish lords were snobs and wouldn't follow a commoner like him.

40. Hammer.

Question of the century

41. At the bottom! Boring answer: he signed it on the meadows of Runnymede by the Thames. Really boring answer: he didn't sign it because he couldn't write – he fixed his seal to it.

Castle cwiz

42. f) The leather skins were hard to set alight.

43. a) Forget the stories of boiling oil – oil was too valuable.

44. j) Elastic hadn't been invented.

45. b) The smell kept the moths away.

46. i) These machines (called 'malvoisins') were fire-proofed with wet leather.

47. d) The 'tortoise' was an umbrella of shields, not a pet in a pie-crust.

48. h) The heads were from captured defenders, of course.

49. e) If they took their furniture every time they moved then they didn't have to worry about having it pinched.

50. c) If the attackers climbed the walls then they could find themselves dumped in a dungeon through a false floor.

51. g) The straw was lowered over the wall to 'cushion' the blows from the ram.

Odd one out

52. Soap factory – Right. In Sopars Lane London, 1259.

53. Hand gun – Wrong. First reported in 1338.

54. Glass factory – Right. First set up in Chiddingfold, Surrey, in 1229.

55. Water pipes – Right. Water was piped in Paddington in 1233.

56. Guillotine – Wrong. First reported in Ireland in 1307, but it wasn't known as a 'guillotine' until the French Revolution.

57. Windmill – Right. Common in Norfolk in the 1260s.

58. Clock – Right. First made in Britain at Dunstable Priory in 1283.

59. Vicar – Right. First seen in Gloucestershire, 1205.

60. Elephant – Right. Given as a gift to King Henry in 1256.

61. Knitting – Wrong. Norfolk 1533.

62. Spectacles – Right. Invented around 1287 in Italy.

63. Hymn book – Wrong. 1501.

64. Sack of sugar – Right. Moroccan sugar on sale in Durham 1299.

65. Glass mirror – Right. Described by a monk in 1279.

66. Cabbage – Wrong. 1531.

67. Pillory – Right. Wallingford 1231.

Knight rules OK

68–77. Numbers 70 and 73 were the only rules! These were real war games and sometimes they got very nasty indeed.

Potty prizes

78 – 87. All are true except 79, 81 and 87.

Ropey relics

88–100. All are true except 90, 95 and 99.

The 1300s
The putrid plague

The 1300s saw the beginning of the Hundred Years War (that didn't last a hundred years). But plague – the Black Death – killed far, far more people than the worst of wars. War, plague . . . and misery for millions.

Quick questions

1. In 1301 King Edward I's son, Edward, was proclaimed a prince. But he wasn't proclaimed Prince of England. Instead he was named prince of where? (Clue: not the Prince of Dolphins)

2. In 1305 you could go to London, Newcastle, Berwick, Edinburgh and Perth and see Scots' leader William Wallace. How? (Clue: he didn't divide his time between the five places)

3. William Wallace was accused of killing anyone who did what? (Clue: if you can read this book then he'd probably kill you!)

4. Barbers in the early 1300s were also surgeons. Their main job was to use their razors to let bad blood out of a sick person's body. What did they put at their shop front to advertise their business? (Clue: it's all in vein)

5. In France in 1314 the leader of the Knights Templar cursed French King Philip and the Pope. The two cursed men died within months. But what had they done to the leader of the Knights Templar? (Clue: made things hot for him)

6. King Edward I's treasure (worth £100,000) was stolen from its closely guarded cellar under Westminster Abbey. How had the thieves got in? (Clue: they wormed their way in)

7. The man who stole Edward I's riches, Richard de Podlicote, was caught and hanged. What was placed on the church door as a warning to anyone else who wanted to try robbing Big Ed? (Clue: a-skin for trouble)

8. Edward I brought law and order to England. How did they say he dealt with a leading outlaw who was robbing travellers? (Clue: king of the road)

9. In 1306 the Countess of Buchan upset Edward III by helping to crown Robert Bruce the King of Scotland. She wasn't killed but was punished in an unusual way. How? (Clue: locked in and locked out)

10. In 1306 Edward I called 300 young men to be knighted at Westminster. But only 298 left the ceremony. Why? (200's company but 300's a crowd)

11. As Edward I lay dying in 1307 he asked his friends to carry him into battle – after he was dead! How did he want them to do this? (Clue: no hide in place)

12. In 1314 the Scots were still fighting the new English king, Edward II. Scot James Douglas captured Roxburgh castle with a trick. What? (Clue: hide in places!)

13. In 1317 the Scots attacked Ireland. What did the Irish do to their capital Dublin to stop the Scots taking it? (Clue: they gave them a warm welcome?)

14. In an Irish witchcraft trial of 1327 Dame Alice was accused of murdering her first three husbands, and poisoning the present one, through magic. She caught a burglar, they say, cut off his head, and used his skull for what? (Clue: eye of bat, perhaps?)

15. Edward II was jailed by his own wife, Isabella, in 1327. Underneath his cell the corpses of dead prisoners were left to rot. Why? (Clue: Isabella didn't want him to stay in jail)

16. Edward II's friend, Hugh Despenser, was hoisted on to a 15-metre-high scaffold and a fire was lit beneath it. What did Hugh see burned on the fire before he was hung? (Clue: it spoiled his breakfast)

17. Edward III was a bad pupil when he was young. What did he do as he read a book, disgusting his teacher? (Clue: crumbs, you shouldn't do that!)

18. In 1330 Edward III avenged his father's death by having his mother's boyfriend, Roger Mortimer, arrested and executed. Mortimer had been safe inside his castle. How did Edward's men get to him? (Clue: it's a secret)

19. In 1337 Edward III claimed to be King of France. The French disagreed and the Hundred Years War started . How long did it last? (Clue: not a hundred years!)

20. In the 1346 Battle of Crécy, the French crossbows faced the English longbows. A thunder storm soaked the crossbow strings and spoiled them. Why didn't it soak the English longbow strings? (Clue: English archers had them and so do snooker tables)

21. At Crécy King John of Bohemia went into battle tied to one of his knights on either side. Why? (Clue: couldn't find his own way)

22. With Edward III fighting in France, the Scots invaded northern England in 1346. They attacked the small English force they saw on a hill at Nevilles Cross, Durham, but the Scots were well beaten. What did they do wrong? (Clue: look before you leap)

23. In 1347 King Edward III danced with Countess Salisbury and part of her clothing dropped off. The king awarded this as a new honour for knights. What did she lose? (Clue: pull your socks up, Countess)

24. In 1349 the planets Saturn, Mars and Jupiter were blamed for what? (Clue: it's an ill wind)

25. In 1360 the Scottish king had a girlfriend, Katherine Mortimer. The Scottish lords didn't like her so what did they do to her? (Clue: give her a short, sharp punishment)

26. At the 1360 Battle of Poitiers the French knights decided to attack the English army on foot. What happened? (Clue: nightfall)

27. In 1360 Edward III abandoned the war against France because so many of his army's horses were killed. By what? (Clue: an ice way to die)

28. Edward III wanted his people to practise their archery in their spare time. In 1363 he banned other sports on public holidays. Two years in prison for playing what? (Clue: from goal to gaol)

29. Edward III wanted to bring back the good old days of King Arthur and his noble knights. What did Ed have made? (Clue: he proved he wasn't a square)

30. John le Cros was a friend of the English Prince of Wales. In 1370 he swapped sides and defended the town of Limoges for the French. When the Prince of Wales captured Limoges what did he do to the innocent townspeople and to guilty John? (Clue: not fair)

31. In 1372 a Spanish fleet defeated an English one. They rammed the English ships then sprayed them with oil. Why? (Clue: a flaming nuisance for the English)

32. In 1375 Sir William Cantilupe was murdered in his bed in Lincoln. But his killers cunningly made it look like he'd been attacked by highway robbers. How? (Clue: dressed to kill)

33. In 1376 Edward III died and ten-year-old Richard II was crowned the following year. He walked into Westminster but was carried out. Why? (Clue: zzzzz)

34. One of the curious rumours that was going around was that Richard II was born without what? (Clue: you can have sausages like this, but not humans)

35. In 1381 Richard's government charged an unpopular 'Poll Tax' of four pence for every person. A rebellion was led by a man called Tyler. What was his first name? (Clue: Yes, it is!)

36. The rebels captured the Archbishop of Canterbury. How did they fasten the bishop's hat on to his head? (Clue: suitable for a wooden head perhaps)

37. In 1393 a cook book suggested a recipe for a common wild animal that would taste like chicken. What? (Clue: privet pig?)

38. Richard II's wife Anne died at Sheen Palace in 1394 and he was so upset he did what? (Clue: turns the palace into a flat?)

39. In Scotland in the 1390s two clans had a dispute. How did the king settle it? (Clue: gladiators)

40. The end of the century brought the end for Richard II. In September 1399 he was forced to give up his throne to Henry IV. If he burst into tears then something he had invented would come in useful. What? (Clue: who nose if he really did invent it?)

Suffering spells

Life was dangerous in the 1300s and people turned to magical spells to help them along. A woman's hair had magical powers – if you had the right chant. The trouble is some words are missing. Get them in the right place and the spell may work. Get them wrong and you'll probably turn into a frog – or worse, a teacher.

Take a lock of woman's hair
Burn it in the open _____ (41).
_____(42) and _____(43) won't come near,
For the _____(44) they truly fear.
Rub the burnt hair in sore _____(45),
Or on _____(46), and they will fly.
Mix some _____(47) with the _____(48),
It will cure a _____(49)'s _____(50).

NEVER TOUCH A TEACHER. YOU'LL GET WARTS!

If you need some help then here are the words . . . in the wrong order, of course.
smoke, warts, baby, serpents, ash, honey, eyes, air, rash, snakes

Question of the century

51. The peasants revolted against the Poll Tax. They cut off the heads of lords and hoisted them up on long thin sticks. How did they fasten them on?

Out of time

Which of these things were first seen in the 1300s? Answer yes or no. . .

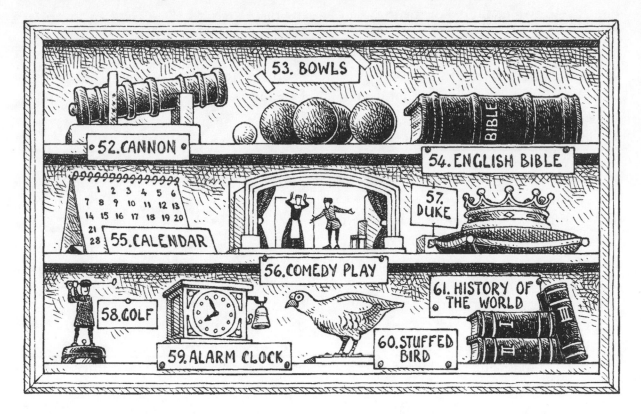

Putrid plague

When the plague arrived in 1349 no one knew how it was caused. They thought you could catch it by looking at a victim, by breathing bad air or drinking from poisoned wells. And they'd no idea how to cure it. But they *did* know what happened to people who had it!

62–71 Can you arrange the terrible ten symptoms in the right order?

a) painful swellings in the groin, the armpits or the neck
b) the victim turns purple
c) the swellings grow to the size of a chicken's egg
d) exhausted feeling
e) death
f) headache
g) fast pulse rate and fast breathing
h) aching joints
i) high temperature and shivering
j) sickness

Clueless cures

The people of the 1300s didn't know how to cure the plague but made some weird guesses. Which of the following did they actually try? Answer true or false.

72. Sniff scented flowers.
73. Kill all the town's cats and dogs.
74. Wear a magpie's beak around your neck.
75. Build huge bonfires in the street to burn the bad air.
76. Drill a hole in your head to let out evil spirits.
77. Don't drink from any well because it could be poisoned.
78. Sleep on your side because sleeping on your back lets foul air run into your nose.
79. Drink cream mixed with the blood from a black cat's tail.
80. Eat onions, leeks and garlic.
81. Eat ten-year-old treacle mixed with marigold flowers and powdered egg.
82. Stop having baths or shaves or a change of clothes.

83. Run away to the countryside where the air is fresh.
84. Throw sweet-smelling herbs on a fire to clean the air.
85. Sit in a sewer so the bad air of the plague is driven off by the worse air of the drains.

86. Swallow powders of crushed emeralds.
87. Eat arsenic powder.
88. Try letting blood out of your body (when your horoscope is right).
89. Shave a live chicken's bottom and strap it to the plague sore.
90. March from town to town flogging yourself with a whip to drive out devils.

Middle Ages mind-benders

A muddled monk wrote these facts about the Middle Ages. But he jumbled the words and he added one word to each sentence that doesn't belong there! Can you sort the words into the right order? (Clue: the odd word out is always in the same position in the sentence)

91. Brides threw over the guests sawdust wedding cake.
92. Teachers were allowed to stab their students not Mondays.
93. A rider road and drowned his horse in a hole in the head.
94. An umbrella used his foot as a giant single snail.
95. The Count of Armagnac broke his bones in a wife's row boat.
96. A pantry looked panter after the castle crumbled.
97. Walter Tyler's proper rebel name was Wat luck.
98. Barrel boys' at St Paul's school collected a pee in the teachers hats.
99. Heads polished their stone with a monks habit.
100. Calais Dick Whittington was twice mayor of London.

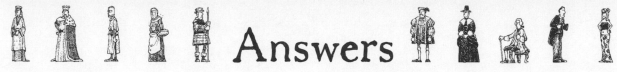

Answers

Quick questions

1. Prince of Wales. It's a title that has been given to an English monarch's oldest son ever since.

2. He was executed and his body was divided, then put on display – head in London, and an arm or a leg in the other four towns.

3. Spoke English. Nonsense, but he was never allowed to speak in his own defence. (If Wallace had spoken in English would he have to kill himself?)

4. A dish of blood. This disgusting display was banned in 1307.

5. They burned him alive for witchcraft, over a slow fire. In fact it was an excuse to destroy the Templars and steal their money. As he burned he cursed them and the curse appeared to work!

6. They dug a tunnel. The monks at Westminster were suspected of being part of the plot.

7. De Podlicote's skin was stretched across the church door. The monks who almost certainly helped with the robbery got away scot free.

8. Ed rode out and took on the outlaw in a fight. He beat him and made the road safe. (This is probably not a true story, though)

9. She was locked in a cage which was hung over the outside of Berwick Castle wall. She was to suffer this punishment for five years and survive!

10. Two knights died in the crush.

11. Ed wanted his body to be boiled till the flesh dropped off and his skeleton to be carried into battle. When he died his family refused to allow it.

12. His soldiers disguised themselves as cattle! Under the cover of the skins they got close enough to surprise the guards.

13. The Irish set Dublin on fire. The Scots gave up and went off to wreck other Irish towns.

14. The skull was used to boil up a witch's brew, her accusers said. Dame Alice's helpers were burned alive, but she escaped to England.

15. Isabella hoped the foul air would infect Edward and kill him. It didn't. In the end she simply ordered him to be murdered.

16. Hugh Despenser had to watch his own guts being burned.

17. He ate while he read and spilled fruit and cheese on to the page. He also let his nose dribble on to the book. 'Snot very nice.

18. They were told about a secret passage into the castle – a bit like something out of an Enid Blyton book!

19. 116 years.

20. The English popped the bowstrings in their pockets till the rain had stopped.

21. King John was blind. To fight was brave but stupid and he was, of course, killed.

22. The small force of English was just the front line. A much larger force was waiting behind the hill. King David of Scotland hid under a bridge but he was captured.

23. Her garter. Edward created the Order of the Garter for knights and it is still awarded today.

24. The plague – also known as the Black Death. The planets lined up in the sky and their evil influence made the air turn bad. Earthquakes were also blamed for releasing poison gases that killed a million in the British Isles in one year.

25. Katherine was stabbed to death.

26. The French were cut down. They didn't understand that knights could *defend* quite well on foot but they were too slow and clumsy to try and attack without their horses. French King John was captured and Poitiers was a French disaster.

27. Hailstones. Huge freak ice-balls battered the horses to death.

28. Football. 'Stickball' (like cricket), handball and cock-fighting were also banned.

29. A round table.

30. The Prince of Wales had the people massacred but spared the life of John.

31. The Spanish fired flaming arrows at the oil-covered English and destroyed the ships.

32. They took him out of his bed, dressed him in riding clothes (including spurs) took him four miles from home and dumped his body in a field by the roadside. His family and servants were suspected but no one was found guilty. A case for Sherlock Holmes?

33. Richard collapsed under the strain of the excitement – and the heavy robes and crown.

34. A skin! He was supposed to have been wrapped in a goat skin to save his life! Weird.

35. Wat.

36. With a nail. It didn't hurt the archbishop

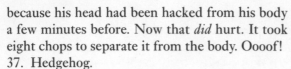

because his head had been hacked from his body a few minutes before. Now that *did* hurt. It took eight chops to separate it from the body. Ooooof!

37. Hedgehog.

38. Flattened the palace. He also got cross at the funeral and smacked Lord Arundel in the face for turning up late.

39. With a fight to the death between 30 warriors from each clan. They had to fight until one side was exterminated. The king watched this grisly 'sport'. Even the winners were left with only 11 men standing.

40. The handkerchief.

Suffering spells

41. Air 42. Snakes 43. Serpents 44. Smoke 45. Eyes 46. Warts 47. Honey 48. Ash 49. Baby 50. Rash

Question of the century

51. They used pole tacks!

Out of time

52. Cannon – Yes. Used in 1331 in Germany and 1346 at Crecy by the English.

53. Bowls – Yes. First mentioned in 1388 when they were banned.

54. English Bible – Yes. Translated in 1384 by John Wycliffe.

55. Calendar – No. 1454, Germany.

56. Comedy play – No. Recorded in Italy in 1389 but first seen in Ancient Greece.

57. Duke – Yes. The first in Britain was the Duke of Cornwall in 1337.

58. Golf – No. First mentioned in 1457 in Scotland but the Romans played a very similar game.

59. Alarm clock – Yes. Made in Germany in 1390 for a monastery to wake up the monks for prayers.

60. Stuffed bird – No. 1517, Amsterdam.

61. History of the world – Yes. 1311, Persia.

Putrid plague

62.f) 63.j) 64.h)

65.a) These are called 'buboes' and that's where the name 'Bubonic' Plague comes from.

66.i) 67.g) 68.d) 69.c) 70.b) 71.e)

Clueless cures

72–90. ALL are true except 74 (a cure for toothache), 76 (a cure for a headache) and 79 (a cure for a cough).

Middle Ages mind-benders

91. Wedding guests threw sawdust over the brides. (If you go to a wedding today then you might throw confetti over the bride for luck. In the Middle Ages the guests threw sawdust.)

92. Students were not allowed to stab their teachers. (It was forbidden to knife an examiner just because he asked you a hard question!)

93. A rider and his horse drowned in a hole in the road. (A miller dug clay from the middle of the road to mend his house. The hole filled with water after a storm and a travelling glove-maker fell in and drowned – along with his horse.)

94. A giant used his single foot as an umbrella. (Superstitious people believed in monsters, such as the one-legged 'Sciapod'. He lay on his back stuck his leg in the air and sheltered under the shadow of his huge foot.)

95. The Count of Armagnac broke his wife's bones in a row. (He was trying to persuade her to sign over some land. After beating her he threw her in a dungeon. This was gentle persuasion.)

96. A panter looked after the castle pantry. (He could have been named after the place where he worked – or he could have been a panter because he had to run up and down all those castle stairs!)

97. Rebel Wat Tyler's proper name was Walter. (He could have been called a Wally.)

98. Teachers at St Paul's school collected the boys' pee in a barrel. (It was sold to leather workers to soften the leather. So if your shoes are hard and uncomfortable, you know what to do? Limp.)

99. Monks polished their heads with a stone. (It was a stone called 'pumice'. The slaphead monks would have used sandpaper if it had been invented.)

100. Dick Whittington was twice mayor of Calais. (Dick Whittington was a real person. Everyone knows the story of Dick and his cat and the bells that said, 'Turn again Whittington and you shall be Lord Mayor of London three times.' BUT not a lot of people know that he was also mayor of Calais – twice!)

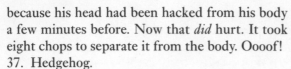

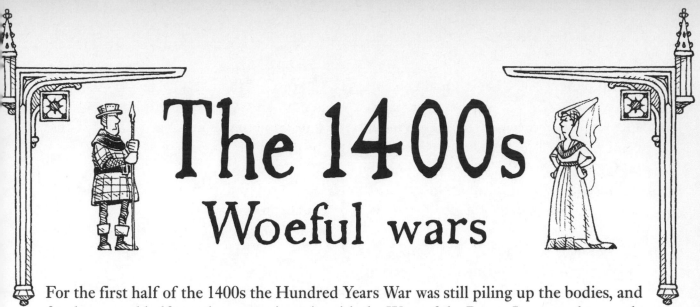

The 1400s
Woeful wars

For the first half of the 1400s the Hundred Years War was still piling up the bodies, and for the second half people were at it again with the Wars of the Roses. It seems the people just had to be bashing someone or other . . . nothing changes, does it?

Quick questions

1. The 1400s were just six days old when Richard II died. He had been a prisoner of the new king, Henry IV. How did Richard die? (Clue: he has no stomach for a fight)

2. People believed Henry IV had Richard II murdered. How did Henry try to prove Richard died naturally? (Clue: see for yourself)

3. Richard's queen, Isabella of France, was quite young to be a widow. How old was she when Richard died? (Clue: double figures)

4. Henry IV soon faced a rebellion from Richard's supporters. Henry defeated them. What did he do to his enemies? (Clue: gave them the sack!)

5. There were rumours that England was cursed by Henry IV's killing of Richard. Stories were told of a boy being born with one eye in his forehead and a calf with two what? (Clue: what a tale)

6. Henry was said to be cursed too. His hair wouldn't grow. Why not? (Clue: it's a lousy reason)

7. In 1401 a new law condemned to death any 'heretic' who refused to repent and obey the Church. The first heretic found guilty under the new law died in March. How? (Clue: sticks not stones)

8. In 1402 Henry went to church to marry Joan of Navarre. In fact he went into church and married a man! Why? (Clue: Joan wasn't around)

9. In 1409 the English attacked Welsh rebels and besieged them in Harlech Castle. The Welsh starved in there for months. How did the English outside the castle torment the hungry Welsh inside? (Clue: a blow to the nose)

10. Henry collapsed in Westminster Abbey in 1413 and was carried to the Jerusalem Chamber. His servants told him where he was and he knew he was

about to die. How? (Clue: I told you so!)

11. Henry had asked to be buried at Canterbury. The roads were so bad his body was sent by ship. What did the sailors do when the ship hit a fierce storm? (Clue: man overboard?)

12. Henry's wife, Joan, spent four years in jail, accused of plotting to kill her step-son, Henry V. How was she supposed to have been trying to kill him? (Clue: does she have a black cat?)

13. When Joan died in 1437 all the lions at the Tower of London died too. She got the blame. Why? (Clue: big cats)

14. Henry V took the throne in 1413 and married Catherine. Two hundred and thirty years later the writer Samuel Pepys kissed her. How? (Clue: everyone likes a kiss from their mummy)

15. The Burgundians envied the English Knights of the Garter so they invented their own order of knights. Knights of the Golden . . . what? (Clue: the knights look a little sheepish)

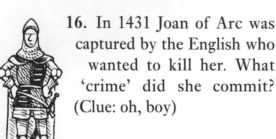

16. In 1431 Joan of Arc was captured by the English who wanted to kill her. What 'crime' did she commit? (Clue: oh, boy)

17. In 1437 James I of Scotland tried to flee from assassins by crawling through a sewer. What stopped him? (Clue: dinners)

18. In 1437 the Earl of Athol assassinated James I and was 'crowned' in Edinburgh. The crowning killed him. How? (Clue: the crown wasn't cold gold)

19. In 1440 James II of Scotland had dinner with the Earl of Douglas and found an extra use for his knife. What? (Clue: don't try this at home)

20. In 1450 Charles VII of France boasted, 'I have the greatest number of veuglaires, serpentines, crapaudines, culverines and ribaudequins that have ever been collected in the history of man.' What did he have? (Clue: Fire!)

21. Henry VI sat at the head of his parliament. But he sat where no English king has sat before or since. Where? (Clue: another kiss from mummy)

22. Henry VI was mentally ill like his grandfather, Charles VI of France. Charles had metal rods fitted inside his clothes in case he fell over and fell apart. Why did he believe this might happen? (Clue: he was *clearly* a sick man)

23. In 1450 rebels rioted in London and cut off the heads of the Sheriff of Kent and his father-in-law. They stuck the heads on poles. The greatest cheer came when the rebels made the two dead heads do what? (Clue: head to head)

24. In 1460 King James II of Scotland attacked Roxburgh Castle with his favourite weapon, a cannon. What did James destroy with his last shot? (Clue: he missed the castle)

25. In 1461 Henry VI's army was defeated in a savage battle, at Towton near Leeds. Soldiers climbed over corpses to get at the enemy. What is the meadow at Towton called today? (Clue: thicker than a water meadow)

26. 440 years after Henry VI's death in the Tower of London, his coffin was opened and historians found proof that he was a murder victim. Where did they find blood? (Clue: a hard place to stab)

27. Edward IV was as tough and ruthless as Henry VI was weak and feeble. He even had his own brother George killed for plotting. How was George said to have died? (Clue: he was a heavy drinker)

28. In May 1464 Edward IV went out hunting but that was just a pretence. In fact he came back with a catch that no one expected. What? (Clue: a dear?)

29. James III of Scotland was kidnapped, then rescued by his brother. How did James try to reward his brother? (Clue: with a meal to end all meals)

30. In 1483 young Edward V took the throne for just 11 weeks before his Uncle Richard III took it from him. No one knows what really happened but there was a story that Ed's mattress in the Tower of London played a part in his death. How? (Clue: Edward is more than mothered)

31. Richard III reigned for just two years

before he was killed on the battlefield by Henry VII's army. The night before the battle something told him he would lose. What? (Clue: Not a peaceful knight)

32. Henry VII made England wealthy, but the buckles on his wife's shoes were made of what? (Clue: a rare metal for a queen)

33. Henry VII had an unpopular palace pet. It disgraced itself by tearing up his diaries. What sort of pet was this? (Clue: look in a mirror?)

34. In 1487 Henry captured a rebel, Lambert Simnel, and kept him in an unusual place. Where? (Clue: Simnel was a bit of a pudding anyway)

35. In 1488 James III of Scotland was wounded in a battle against his son, James IV. He asked for a priest to help him. What did the priest help him to do? (Clue: a heavenly job)

36. James IV of Scotland was curious about science. He wanted to experiment with medicine and dentistry himself. He paid a man 70p to let him do what? (Clue: he looked a little down in the mouth)

37. Henry VII was the first Tudor monarch. The Tudors said they could trace their family back to the days of an ancient British king who is now famous in a nursery rhyme. Who? (Clue: fiddles)

38. Henry had the simple-minded Duke of Warwick executed in 1499. On his way from his prison cell to the block, what did the daft Duke do? (Clue: no good at geography)

39. Henry had a fortune-teller locked in the Tower. What had the man said that upset the king? (Clue: a grave error)

40. In pictures of Henry VII he is never smiling. Why not? (Clue: shy)

Question of the century
41. Why was King Edward IV buried at Windsor?

Cool cures

The plague was past its worst by the 1400s but there were other nasty illnesses that needed treating. The doctors of the 1400s were still quite clueless. Can you match the illness to the right cure?

ILLNESS

42. RINGWORM

43. GOUT

44. PLAGUE

45. SKIN DISEASE

46. LOSS OF MEMORY

47. SLEEPLESSNESS (INSOMNIA)

48. BRUISES

49. FAINTING

50. BLOCKED UP NOSE

51. BLEEDING INSIDE THE BODY

Foul foods

Which of the following would some people eat in the 1400s? Answer true or false. . .

52. Vultures
53. Chips
54. Cucumber
55. Fruit jelly
56. Tomatoes

57. Whale meat
58. Starlings
59. Cakes
60. Cornflakes
61. Porpoises

News of the World

Can you complete these headlines from the world of the 1400s?

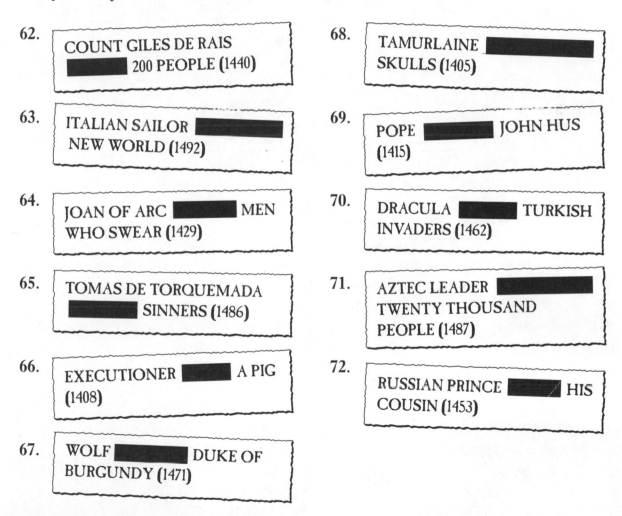

62. COUNT GILES DE RAIS ▊▊▊ 200 PEOPLE (1440)

63. ITALIAN SAILOR ▊▊▊ NEW WORLD (1492)

64. JOAN OF ARC ▊▊▊ MEN WHO SWEAR (1429)

65. TOMAS DE TORQUEMADA ▊▊▊ SINNERS (1486)

66. EXECUTIONER ▊▊▊ A PIG (1408)

67. WOLF ▊▊▊ DUKE OF BURGUNDY (1471)

68. TAMURLAINE ▊▊▊ SKULLS (1405)

69. POPE ▊▊▊ JOHN HUS (1415)

70. DRACULA ▊▊▊ TURKISH INVADERS (1462)

71. AZTEC LEADER ▊▊▊ TWENTY THOUSAND PEOPLE (1487)

72. RUSSIAN PRINCE ▊▊▊ HIS COUSIN (1453)

Clues: here are the words that fit the spaces . . . but not in the right order.
horrifies, burns, executes, eats, sacrifices, murders, blinds, hangs, discovers, collects, banishes

Groovy games

Which of these modern pastimes were played (in some form) in the 1400s? Answer yes or no.

Weird words

Books began to be printed in English and people could read the horrible sufferings of the peasants – though the peasants themselves probably wouldn't have been able to read. William Langland wrote a poem about a peasant called 'Piers Ploughman' and his miserable life. Can you work out just how miserable from this part of the poem? Some of the words have been scrambled by a careless printer – well, the first book printed in English was produced in 1475, so he hadn't had a lot of practice.

The Peasant
His coat of a cloth that is NITH (91) as the East wind,
His DOHO (92) full of holes with his HARI (93) sticking through,
His clumsy HOSSE (94), knobbled and nailed over thickly,
Yet his SOTE (95) poked clean through as he trod on the ground.
Two miserable mittens made out of old GRAS (96),
The fingers worn out and the FHLIT (97) caked on them,
He waded in mud almost up to his KLANSE (98),
In front are four NOXE (99), so weary and feeble
Their BRIS (100) could be counted, so wretched they were.

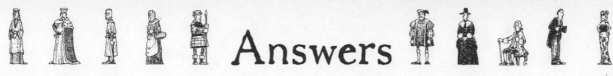

Answers

Quick questions

1. He starved himself to death, some said. Others said he'd been starved on the orders of the king.
2. Richard's body was paraded through London in an open coffin.
3. Isabella was just ten years old. She was only seven when she married him.
4. Not only did he have them executed but they were chopped up, put in sacks and sent to London.
5. Tails. There was also a story of eggs being cooked and opened to show the face of a man with white hair – but it was probably just a funny yoke.
6. Henry's hair was full of lice which he couldn't seem to cure.
7. William Sawtre was burned to death.
8. Joan sent a 'stand-in' who made her marriage vows for her. It wasn't unusual in the Middle Ages. This substitute was usually a man.
9. The English roasted meat and let the breeze carry the delicious smell into the castle.
10. A fortune-teller had told him that he would die in 'Jerusalem'.
11. It is said they threw Henry's body into the sea because he was cursed, and switched it for a dead sailor. It is true that when the coffin was opened in 1832 it contained no riches but only a simple wooden cross. Maybe the sailors did switch the bodies and helped themselves to the royal wealth!
12. Witchcraft.
13. A witch's helpers are supposed to die with the witch and it was said that the lions were Queen Joan's devil-helpers (because a queen witch would need big cats).
14. Catherine's corpse was turned into a mummy and put on show next to the coffin of Henry V. People could look at her for a couple of pennies and she stayed there for almost 300 years. Samuel Pepys kissed the mummy – weird!
15. Fleece. Their badge was a golden sheep hung around the neck. Would ewe believe it?
16. She dressed as a man, which made her a 'heretic' and gave them the excuse to burn her.
17. James was too fat and got stuck. The killers dragged him out and hacked him to death. That's one way to lose weight.
18. The crown was red-hot iron. It was his punishment for killing the king. His flesh was also pinched with red-hot pincers.
19. He stabbed the earl. He considered him a traitor and servants finished him off with 26 stab wounds. The body was thrown out of the window.
20. Different types of cannon.
21. Henry sat on him mum's knee. He was just eight months old when he took the throne. Some days he had such screaming fits that his visits to parliament had to be cancelled.
22. Charles believed he was made of glass.
23. Kiss.
24. James blew off his own leg and died when the cannon misfired.
25. Bloody Meadow.
26. In Henry's hair. It is said that he was stabbed in the head by the man who became Richard III.
27. George is believed to have been drowned in a barrel of wine. Some say his younger brother, Richard III, did the drowning. And some say that George asked for this method of execution.
28. A wife. He secretly met and married Elizabeth Woodford while he pretended to be hunting. The marriage was so unpopular he kept it secret for four months.
29. He tried to poison him.
30. He was smothered by the mattress. His younger brother died with him and they may have been buried under a stairway at the Tower. Two bodies were unearthed there in 1674.
31. Richard had nightmares about the people he had murdered.
32. Tin. Henry was rich but extremely mean. His wife had to patch and darn her own dresses.
33. A monkey.
34. He was given a job in Henry's castle kitchen.
35. The priest helped him to die by stabbing him. In fact it wasn't a priest but an enemy lord in disguise. Bad luck, James.
36. Take all of his teeth out.
37. Coel Hen Godebog, better known to us as Old King Cole.
38. The Duke almost got lost. He wandered off in the wrong direction. Unfortunately there were guards to lead him to the block.
39. The fortune teller said Henry would be dead before Christmas. He was wrong – and he suffered for it.

40. His teeth were rotten and black.

Question of the century
41. Because he was dead.

Cool cures
42.f) 43.i) 44.a) 45.h) 46.b) 47.e) 48.d) 49.j) 50.c) 51.g)

Foul foods
52–61 All true except for 53 (they had no potatoes), 54 (cucumbers were thought to be unhealthy to eat), 56 (they had no tomatoes) and 60 (they had no maize).

News of the World
62. Murders. One of history's biggest mass murderers, who killed many children. He was strangled and burned for his crimes.
63. Discovers. The Italian was Christopher Columbus.
64. Banishes. Joan said God would be upset by bad language, so any soldiers who swore had to go.
65. Burns. He was Spain's 'Inquisitor' and tortured people to admit they were sinners and burnt them if they refused to 'repent'.
66. Hangs. The pig had killed a girl and the punishment was to be hanged. The executioner even sent a bill to the pig for the rope he used.
67. Eats. The Duke died in battle in Switzerland but wolves got to the body before it could be taken away for burial.
68. Collects. The Asian conqueror, Tamurlaine, piled up the severed heads of his enemies in the centres of defeated towns to show his power. He was clearly a head case.
69. Executes. John Hus had rebelled against the church. The Pope invited him to Rome for a chat. When Hus arrived the Pope had him executed.
70. Horrifies. Transylvanian Prince Vlad Dracula made a habit of capturing Turkish invaders alive, pushing a sharpened stake through them and standing them by the roadside to die. Twenty thousand bodies stretched for a mile in front of the invaders and the shocked Turks gave up.
71. Sacrifices. Ahuitzotl had 20,000 prisoners brought to the great temple and began ripping out their hearts. When he was exhausted his councillors took over.
72. Blinds. Prince Dmitry blinded cousin Vasily, but the kind prince didn't have his cousin killed. He should have done. Vasily raised an army and took his revenge. Dmitry was poisoned and blind Vasily took the throne.

Groovy games
73. Archery – Yes.
74. Kites – Yes.
75. Football – Yes. But not 11-a-side. Whole villages took part in a great punch-up.
76. Throwing quoits – Yes.
77. Golf – Yes. Golf became popular in Scotland and Holland in the 1400s.
78. Tennis – Yes. Tennis balls were not made of soft rubber but solid wood. People struck with tennis balls were known to die.
79. Blind Man's Buff – Yes. It was supposed to have been invented after a French knight called Colin was blinded in a battle but continued fighting by lashing out with his weapons.
80. Ice skating – Yes. Ice skates were made from cattle bones.
81. Hockey – Yes.
82. Bowling – Yes. Bowling at skittles and bowls on grass.
83. Dominoes – Yes.
84. Comics – No. First appeared in 1890.
85. Chess – Yes.
86. Toy windmills – Yes. Popular gifts at the fair.
87. Marbles – Yes. Though the marbles were simply balls of clay, not glass.
88. Draughts – Yes.
89. Cards – Yes.
90. Doll's houses – No. First built in 1588.

Weird words
91. Thin 92. Hood 93. Hair 94. Shoes 95. Toes 96. Rags 97. Filth 98. Ankles 99. Oxen 100. Ribs

The 1500s
The terrible Tudors

This was the century when the Tudor family brought terror to Britain. Brit sailors discovered new worlds and new ways to kill themselves – like tobacco – while Tudor Tower torturers found new ways to make you suffer. Even queenly necks were on the block while Henry's fat bum was on the throne. A truly savage century.

Quick questions

1. In 1502 King James IV of Scotland fell in love with Margaret Drummond, but she died suddenly. What curious thing happened to her sister at the same time? (Clue: double trouble)

2. Henry VIII came to the throne in 1509. Two people had to die so he could become king. Who? (Clue: father and son)

 3. In the 1514 Battle of Flodden between England and Scotland, the Earl of Surrey was carried into battle. Why? (Clue: no zimmer frames)

4. Queen Catherine was in charge of England when her army beat the Scots at Flodden because Henry VIII was in France. The Scottish king was hacked down. What gruesome gift did Catherine send Henry to celebrate the win? (Clue: James would be chilly without it)

5. In 1528 the Protestant Scottish rebel Patrick Hamilton was executed. Why was the damp weather bad news for poor Pat? (Clue: smoking is bad for your health)

6. In 1532 a cook, Richard Rosse, poisoned 17 people with his soup. He should have been hanged but Henry VIII thought of a more suitable way to execute a killer cook. What? (Clue: one for the pot)

7. In 1534 a fortune teller, the Holy Maid of Kent, said that Henry VIII would 'die a villain's death' if he married Anne Boleyn. Henry made sure that the Maid died a villain's death. How? (Clue: knot good)

8. In 1535 Henry's friend Thomas More was beheaded for opposing the king. Thomas warned the executioner about his neck. He said, 'Be careful because it's. . .' What? (Clue: no giraffe)

9. In 1536 Catherine of Aragon died and she was buried in a plain grave. But in

Victorian times a group of ladies clubbed together to buy her a marble gravestone. What did they have in common with the dead queen? (Clue: not called Aragon)

10. In 1536 Queen Anne Boleyn was beheaded but not a drop of blood was spilled on the block. Why not? (Clue: someone swipes Anne's head!)

11. On 4 January '540 Henry VIII was due to marry wife ~o. 4, Anne of Cleves, but he put it off fo wo days. Why? (Clue: you might do this ith homework!)

12. In 1541 Henry headed off to York to meet the Scottish king, James V. What did James do that made Henry furious? (Clue: stand up?)

13. In 1541 the old Countess of Pole went to the block simply because her son was Henry's enemy. Her behaviour was unusual. How? (Clue: catch me if you can)

14. In 1542 Henry had wife no. 5, Catherine Howard, executed for having boyfriends while she was married to him. He also executed Lady Rochford, Cathy's housekeeper. For what? (Clue: Cupid?)

15. In 1545 Henry VIII went to watch his magnificent warship, the *Mary Rose*, set sail to sort out the French. What did *Mary Rose* do to surprise the king? (Clue: behaves in a fishy manner)

16. In September 1546 Henry VIII was very ill. His doctors knew he was dying but they didn't tell him. Why not? (Clue: look what happened to the Holy Maid of Kent)

17. Henry VIII had his dinner delivered to his sick room on 31 January 1547, as he had done for the past month. What was so odd about this delivery? (Clue: he had no appetite)

18. Henry was buried in his huge coffin. There is a gruesome story that Catholic daughter Mary had his corpse dug up. Then what? (Clue: the first of many)

19. Edward VI came to the throne in 1547. Ed's pet dog warned him of a mysterious night-time visitor. What happened to the hero mutt? (Clue: it was a shot in the dark)

20. In Scotland in 1546 a Protestant group entered Cardinal Beaton's room to kill him as revenge for Patrick Hamilton's burning. They started to stab him when a priest with them said, 'Stop! Stop! This is not being done God's way.' What did he make them do? (Clue: they can do it with their eyes closed)

21. Young Edward VI was king but his uncle, Thomas Seymour had been bribing him. With gold? With jewels? No! What could Uncle Tom bribe the King of England with? (Clue: your parents may try this from time to time!)

22. Edward died in 1553 and the powerful Duke of Northumberland tried to make Lady Jane Grey queen. She lasted nine days until Mary Tudor took her throne. Jane went to the block but had trouble finding it. Why? (Clue: in the dark)

23. Northumberland was also executed. The judges said his heart should be cut from his body. What was the executioner to do with it next? (Clue: bit of a cheek)

24. Catholic Mary came to the throne in 1553, and the Protestants showed what they thought of her by leaving something on her bed. What? (Clue: hounding her out of the palace?)

25. Mary married Spanish Prince Philip in 1554. He hated something that came from her nose. What? (Clue: 'snot what you think)

26. Philip left Mary and went to fight in Europe. She tried to tempt him back with what? (Clue: the way to a man's heart is through his stomach, they say)

27. Mary had a lot of Protestant 'heretics' burned. Her chief helper was Reginald Pole who chose really odd 'heretics' to burn. What was odd about them? (Clue: they never felt a thing)

28. Mary sent Archbishop Cranmer to the stake in 1556. He had written an apology then changed his mind. When he saw the fire he did a strange thing. What? (Clue: he went to his death single-handed)

29. Mary died and the news was taken to half-sister Elizabeth, the new queen. They say Elizabeth was reading in the garden when the news came, but that's unlikely. Why? (Clue: remember, remember when Mary died)

30. Elizabeth had a new tax created which only men could pay. It was a tax on what? (Clue: it might grow on you)

31. Elizabeth I's godson, Sir John Harrington, disgraced himself by making rude remarks to her ladies-in-waiting. She banished him. He went off and invented something that was so useful she forgave him. What? (Clue: flushed with success?)

32. In 1576 the explorer Martin Frobisher returned to England with a load of 'black earth'. What use did he think it would be? (Clue: he thinks the soil is rich)

33. Eloye Mestrell invented the first machine in England for making coins for the government. Yet in 1578 he was arrested and executed. What was his crime? (Clue: double your money)

34. Mary Queen of Scots had Sir John Huntly beheaded but then discovered he had to be tried properly and found guilty if she was to get his fortune. What did she do? (Clue: head on over to the courtroom)

35. Mary Queen of Scots became unpopular in Scotland, and fled to England to ask cousin Elizabeth I for protection. How did Liz protect Mary? (Clue: no one can get in to get her)

36. James Douglas of Scotland invented the 'Maiden' machine. In 1581 the Maiden killed him. What was it? (Clue: a chip off the old block)

37. Mary Queen of Scots had lots of troubles. She finally met a man and thanked him for, 'making an end to all my troubles'. What was this man's job? (Clue: not an agony aunt!)

38. When Mary Queen of Scots was beheaded in 1587 her head was supposed to have been lifted high in the air by the executioner to prove she was dead. But he dropped it. Why? (Clue: hair today, gone tomorrow)

39. In 1591 King James of Scotland was caught in a storm. He was sure it was a witchcraft plot to kill him. He said he saw hares sailing through the storm. What were they floating in? (Clue: the Jumblies went to sea in the same thing!)

40. Playwrights like Shakespeare didn't make much money in the 1590s when plagues closed the theatres. What did the playwright Kit Marlowe do to make extra cash? (Clue: with my little eye)

Awful Aztecs

In 1519 the Spaniards arrived in Mexico and met the Aztecs. These people made the Tudors look like harmless hamsters. Apart from their horrible habit of human sacrifice, how much do you know about the Aztecs? Answer true or false.

41. Aztec warriors wore metal armour.

42. Aztec priests cut out the hearts of sacrifice victims with a glass knife.
43. Boys were trained to be warriors and were given battle dress when they were still babies.
44. Aztec warriors believed they would become hummingbirds if they died in battle.
45. The Aztecs had public toilets.
46. Warriors with long hair were seen as the best fighters.
47. Aztecs liked to eat scum.
48. An Aztec boy had to ask his best friend for permission to get married.
49. Young Aztec men could be made full warriors by having their faces smeared with the blood of a heart that was still beating.
50. The Spanish caught terrible diseases from the Aztec people.

Horrible Henry

Henry VIII was one of Britain's cruellest monarchs ever. Here's a quick quiz to test your brains. Get one wrong and your head goes on the block. . .

THAT'S WHAT YOU GET WHEN YOU TAKE ON A TUDOR!

51. When wife no. 1, Catherine of Aragon, died Henry had a...?
a) ball
b) fight
c) cup of tea

52. Wife no. 2, Anne Boleyn, needed the toilet a lot during her coronation. Her ladies-in-waiting kept her potty handy...?
a) under the table
b) in a room close by
c) on the throne

53. When Anne gave birth to a daughter, Henry...?
a) sulked
b) cheered
c) fell out of his pram

54. While Anne was being beheaded, Henry was playing...?
a) tennis
b) music
c) the fool

55. Henry divorced wife no. 4, Anne of Cleves, because she was...?
a) ugly
b) stupid
c) vegetarian

56. Wife no. 5, Catherine Howard, was sentenced to death for having lovers. She begged for mercy but Heartless Henry locked the door and left her...?
a) to wail
b) in jail
c) looking pale

57. Henry had his old friend Thomas More executed and his head stuck...?
a) over London Bridge
b) under London Bridge
c) in a fridge

58. Henry had Cardinal Fisher beheaded and showed disrespect by leaving the headless body...?
a) naked for a day
b) on the main highway
c) in a window display

59. Henry had an old hunting friend, Cardinal Newdigate, chained in the street. The man couldn't move, even to go to...?
a) the toilet
b) the church
c) the cup final

60. Henry had lots of trouble with rebels, so he had hung from church steeples...?
a) rebel monks
b) helpless drunks
c) swimming trunks

Painful punishments

What would you do to someone who sold you a theatre ticket . . . for a play that was never performed? Match these true Tudor crimes and punishments to find out what would have happened in terrible Tudor times. . .

CRIME	PUNISHMENT
61. Fraud. Richard Vennor sold tickets for a play that never took place.	**a)** Pressing. Lain on the ground with weights piled on top.
62. Fortune telling. In 1578 Sallow Kenneth went to Lady Seaforth and told her that her husband was flirting with other women in France.	**b)** Skeffington's gyves. An iron hoop in two halves joined by a hinge. The prisoner, hands tied behind, knelt in one half while the torturer closed the second half shut. The prisoner was squeezed into a tight ball.
63. Refusing to speak in court. Margaret Clitheroe refused to plead guilty or not-guilty when she was accused of hiding Catholic priests.	**c)** Thumbscrews. The victim's thumbs were placed under a metal bar. The bar was slowly screwed down so it squeezed the finger nails.
64. Witchcraft. In 1596 Scot Thomas Papley was accused of witchcraft and refused to confess.	**d)** The hole. Thrown into jail to sleep on bare boards with 50 other prisoners – freezing in winter and suffocating in summer.
65. Spying. England was full of spies from Spain and France who reported back to their masters. It was important to get them to talk before they died.	**e)** The gauntlets. The prisoner was stood on blocks of wood. His (or her) wrists were fastened in iron handcuffs to a beam above their head. One by one the blocks were removed till the prisoner was standing on tiptoe and finally swinging from the beam.
66. Being a Catholic priest. Banned by Elizabeth I. When one was caught he'd be tortured to betray names and hiding places of other Catholics.	**f)** Whipping stocks. Given twelve strokes on their bare back with a whip with two cords, but without any knots. The victims then were dragged through the streets and locked in the stocks at Cheapside where the crowds could pelt them with rubbish and spit at them.

67. Child cruelty. Eliza Morton was taken in to the poor-house to work because she was a beggar. Then it was discovered she had a child but had left her on the streets in the hope someone would care for her

g) The barrel. Popped into a tar barrel lined with spikes. It was set on fire and rolled down a hill.

68. Treason. Prisoners suspected of plotting against the monarch were often tortured so they would name their fellow-plotters.

h) The boot. Had a metal book placed over the foot and wedges driven in till the ankle bones were crushed and splintered.

Question of the century

69. Why would it be better to die like Joan of Arc than Anne Boleyn?

Would you believe it?

Queen Elizabeth I ruled from 1558 to 1603. There are lots of stories about this famous queen, but which of these tall tales are true and which false. . .?

70. She threatened to pass a law banning her courtiers from wearing long cloaks.
71. She died because of a rotten tooth.
72. Elizabeth was overjoyed when her sister, Mary, died.
73. She liked to read her horoscope.
74. Elizabeth ate a chessboard.
75. She had regular baths.

76. Elizabeth never even considered getting married.
77. Elizabeth had beautiful red hair.
78. She was always true to her Protestant faith.
79. She punched and kicked her secretary.

Fifteen hundreds firsts

Which of these things might you have seen in the 1500s? Answer yes or no ...

Ingenious insults

Can you match the words in these columns to come up with ten insults that Shakespeare put into his plays? WARNING: Do NOT call your teacher any of these names.

91.	taffeta	**a)**	lump
92.	scurvy	**b)**	ape
93.	red-tailed	**c)**	chuff
94.	threadbare	**d)**	bumble-bee
95.	mad-headed	**e)**	punk
96.	fat	**f)**	juggler
97.	false	**g)**	crookback
98.	bloodsucker of	**h)**	caterpillars
99.	scolding	**i)**	sleeping men
100.	deformed	**j)**	lord

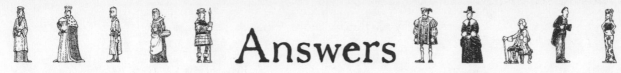

Answers

Quick questions

1. Margaret's sister died at the same time. It's a fair bet they were both poisoned. James went on to marry Henry VIII's sister instead.

2. Henry VII (who died in 1509) and also his eldest son, Arthur (who died in 1502).

3. He was 70. The oldest Scot in the battle, William Maitland, actually fought and died – and he was 90!

4. Catherine sent the bloodstained coat from the dead King of Scotland. Henry was furious. He wanted the glory of the victory for himself. There's no pleasing some people.

5. Patrick Hamilton was burned to death but the damp weather meant he burnt slowly. The executioners tried to put gunpowder on the fire but that only scorched him.

6. Henry ordered that Rosse be boiled alive in his own pot. Rosse always said that he put the poison in the pot as a joke – it wasn't meant to kill.

7. She was hanged along with three men who supported her attack on the king.

8. Very short. He asked the executioner to try and be an accurate shot with the axe.

9. They were all called 'Catherine'.

10. Anne wasn't beheaded on a block. She knelt down and her head was removed with a single swipe of a sword. It was said her lips kept moving in prayer for minutes after her head was off.

11. Henry tried to put it off until he could find an excuse not to do it. He didn't want to marry Anne after all, but he knew if he refused he would upset her powerful father. In the end he had to go ahead.

12. James didn't turn up. James' councillors said Henry was planning a trap.

13. She moved her head around to make the job as difficult as possible for the executioner. It took him several chops at her shoulders before he finally hit her neck and got her head off.

14. Lady Rochford arranged the meetings between Catherine and her boyfriends.

15. Rolled over and sank. It may have been top heavy with all the guns and men and the boat was upset. Henry was upset too – but 500 people on board were dead upset. Simply dead, in fact.

16. It was illegal for anyone to say, 'The king is going to die.' So they didn't say it – he died anyway.

17. Henry had died three days earlier on 28 January. The lords wanted his death kept secret for a few days till the throne was safe for Edward VI to take it. They had meals delivered to the room to make it seem normal. But who ate them?

18. She had him burned. Probably not true.

19. The dog was shot dead by the visitor, who was Ed's uncle. He was executed, and the mutt was avenged.

20. Pray. When they finished the prayer they finished off the Bishop. God would be glad about that.

21. Pocket money. It worked for a while but Uncle Tom got power mad and ended up with his neck on the block and his head on the floor.

22. Jane was blindfolded.

23. Throw it in his face! Yeuch!

24. A dead dog. The head was shaved, the ears cropped and a noose put around its neck. The message was clear: 'This is what we do to Catholics.'

25. Philip hated Mary's foul breath. It was an illness she had and not her fault. But it put him off, and he left her broken hearted.

26. His favourite meat pies. She had them sent across the English Channel to him. He ate all the pies but didn't go home for more.

27. They were dead. Reggie dug them up and burned them anyway. Funny feller.

28. He stuck his writing hand in the flames to punish it for writing the apology. (No jokes about second-hand shops, please.)

29. It was November. Not many people are daft enough to sit in the garden in an English winter.

30. Beards.

31. A flushing toilet. It took him six years to invent it but Liz loved his loo.

32. He believed it contained a fortune in gold. It didn't. He was just a clueless captain.

33. Eloye made a second, secret, machine and forged money for himself. Usually forgers had a hand chopped off but Eloye was hanged.

34. Huntly's head was sewn back on and his corpse was put on trial.

35. Elizabeth locked Mary in prison. She left her there for 18 years before deciding to execute her.

36. The Maiden was a type of guillotine. He was executed on it.

37. He was her executioner. Actually he made a

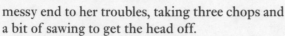

messy end to her troubles, taking three chops and a bit of sawing to get the head off.

38. Mary was wearing a wig. When he grabbed it, the head slipped out and bounced on to the floor.

39. A sieve. No one dared call King James a liar – or plain barmy.

40. Marlowe was a spy. He died in 1593, stabbed in the eye in a fight, possibly because he was mixed up in spying.

Awful Aztecs

41. False. They had armour but it was made of hardened cotton.

42. True. The knives were made from a type of natural glass called 'obsidian'.

43. True. They were given a loincloth, shield, cloak and four arrows when they were a few days old.

44. True. They believed they would hum off to join the Sun God.

45. True. And the human manure would be used as fertilizer for crops.

46. False. Warriors couldn't get their hair cut until they'd killed someone in battle.

47. True. Lake scum was made into cakes.

48. False. He had to ask his teacher!

49. True.

50. False. The Spanish brought diseases from Europe which killed many Aztecs.

Horrible Henry

51–60. All answers are (a). Anyone answering (c) should give up quizzes ... now.

Painful punishments

61. d) Result – survived.

62. g) Result – death.

63. a) Result – death.

64. h) Result – survived and later executed.

65. b) Result – often death. Leonard Skeffington was in charge of the Tower in the days of Henry VIII. This machine could be carried to the prisoner's cell and used there, to save trips to the torture chamber.

66. e) Result – usually survived then executed.

67. f) Result – survived

68. c) Result – survived but hands totally mangled.

Question of the century

69. Because a hot steak is better than a cold chop.

Would you believe it?

70. True. She was terrified of being killed and wanted her courtiers' swords uncovered and ready.

71. False. Elizabeth is famous for having rotten teeth, but that didn't kill her. She caught a cold and never recovered.

72. True. She said, 'This is the Lord's doing and it is marvellous in our eyes.'

73. True. A mathematician (and magician!) called John Dee used to read Liz's horoscope and foretell the future for her.

74. True. Of course, it was made of marzipan.

75. True. Elizabeth did bathe regularly ... once every three months!

76. False. Liz had a few close calls when it came to marriage, including Lord Dudley and the French Duke of Anjou.

77. True and False. She did at first, but she ended up bald with a collection of 80 wigs!

78. False. While Catholic Mary Tudor was queen, Elizabeth said she was a Catholic too.

79. True. Secretary William Davison was just one of the unfortunate palace workers who suffered Liz's temper tantrums.

Fifteen hundreds firsts

80. Fireworks display – Yes. 1572, London.

81. Guy Fawkes Day – No. 1607.

82. Glass eye – Yes. 1578, Venice.

83. Tobacco – Yes. First in Europe in 1556.

84. Cigarettes – No. 1843, France.

85. The ruff – Yes. The fashion arrived from France in 1542.

86. Postal service – Yes. Royal Mail set up in 1512.

87. Postage stamp – No. 1653, Paris.

88. Wrist watch – Yes. Elizabeth had one of the first.

89. Lipstick – No. 1915, though Tudor women did use lip colour.

90 Pencils – Yes. 1584, made of Cumbrian graphite.

Ingenious insults

91.e) 92.j) 93.d) 94.f) 95.b) 96.c) 97.h) 98.i) 99.g) 100.a)

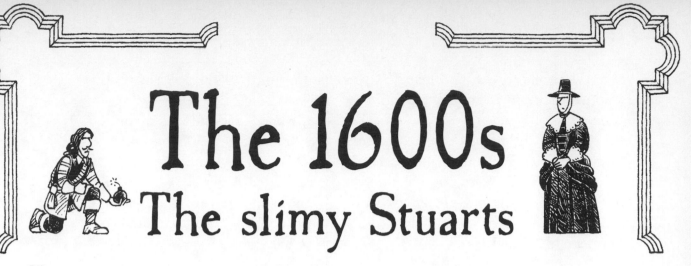

The 1600s
The slimy Stuarts

This was the age when Guy Fawkes failed to get into Parliament, when Charles I was Charles the Chopped, when Oliver Cromwell's Roundheads beat the Cavaliers into Flatheads, and the Great Fire of London did the Great Plague people of London a red hot favour.

Quick questions

1. In Scotland in the 1600s some people threw a cat over a person with a fever. Why? (Clue: it isn't meant to kill the cat)

2. In 1601 Queen Elizabeth's favourite, the Earl of Essex, rebelled. He failed and was sentenced to death. How did Liz show mercy to her dear friend? (Clue: quick and clean)

3. Everyone remembers the Spanish Armada of 1588. Everyone forgets they came back in 1601. Where did they land? (Clue: sounds like they land on an island?)

4. Just before Elizabeth I died she said she wanted James of Scotland to take her throne. This may have partly made up for what she had done to his mother. What? (Clue: shortened her)

5. When the plague returned to London in 1603 people stole hundreds of the best of these to help them. What? (Clue: they wanted a quick get-away)

6. James of Scotland rode down to rule England in 1603. He got a close-up view of his new land when he arrived at Burghley. How? (Clue: still done at Burghley Horse Trials today!)

7. Henry VIII wore a padded jacket for warmth. Why did James I wear one? (Clue: he's afraid of sharp practice)

8. What did snotty King James use instead of a handkerchief? (Clue: your mum probably tells you *not* to do this!)

9. James I put a frog down the neck of his friend, the Earl of Pembroke. The Earl got his revenge by putting what in James' bed? (Clue: he was a real swine)

10. In 1605 Catholic plotters tried to blow up James as he opened Parliament. They planted gunpowder, wood and what other stuff in the cellars? (Clue: from Newcastle?)

11. In 17th century Aberdeen the town hangman also had to deal with tramps.

What did he do with them? (Clue: stopped the tramps hanging around?)

12. In 1610 the King's cousin, Arabella Stuart, married William Seymour secretly. When King James found out he gave the happy couple an unexpected wedding present. What? (Clue: from holy wedlock to unholy dead-locks)

13. In 1611 an English sheep thief could be hanged. But a Scottish rustler, James Watson, suffered an ancient form of punishment for the crime. What? (Clue: the law officers sea him off)

14. In Gloucester in 1612 men arranged themselves into pairs and kicked each other on the shins. Why? (Clue: it's a knockout)

15. In 1613 a cannon set fire to Shakespeare's Globe theatre and burnt it to the ground. Why? (Clue: part of a plot)

16. A 1616 book said they were 'idle', and 'spring from the Devil' and 'their heads, hands, hearts and minds are evil.' What were these horrific creatures? (Clue: half the population?)

17. April 23rd 1616 was William Shakespeare's 52nd birthday. If there was to be a party then he spoiled it by doing what? (Clue: he hadn't the breath to blow out his candles)

18. In 1620 the Pilgrim Fathers were fed up with being pushed around by the English Church. They set sail from Plymouth and landed in America. What is the name of the American port where they landed? (Clue: home sweet home)

19. In 1626 the scientist Francis Bacon killed a chicken and stuffed it with snow to show frozen food would stay fresh. But it killed him. How? (Clue: Sniff! Sniff!)

20. In 1634 a lawyer published a book that offended the king. The book was burned. This was painful for the lawyer. Why? (Clue: it's a punishment not to be sniffed at)

21. At the Civil War battle of Edgehill the famous doctor, William Harvey, settled down with a book as soldiers fell all around him. When he grew cold he pulled what over his legs to keep warm? (Clue: the doctor was no use to them)

22. Charles I was captured by Oliver Cromwell's army and held prisoner in Newcastle. They let him out to play what game in the nearby fields? (Clue: join the club)

23. Charles I went to his execution in 1649 wearing two shirts. Why? (Clue: it was 30 January 1649)

24. Sir Arthur Aston had a wooden leg so he was easily caught in a 1649 Irish battle. He was beaten to death. With what? (Clue: did he put his foot in it?)

25. Oliver Cromwell died in 1658 and the public queued to see his mummified body. But it began to go rotten. What did the government do next? (Clue: you wooden believe it)

26. Charles's head was sewn back on so he'd look good in his coffin. But his tomb was entered many years later and the neck bone stolen. It was used at the dinner table by Henry Halford. For what? (Clue: needed on chops!)

27. In 1653 Charles Culpepper wrote that this plant clears bad chests, cures headaches, worms and indigestion, and the juice kills lice in children's hair. What is this wonder plant? (Clue: it cures nothing and has killed millions)

28. In 1660 Charles II returned and punished the men who had had his dad, Charles I, beheaded. One condemned man had his belly opened and his guts lifted out for burning. How did he shock his executioner? (Clue: you can't keep a good man down)

29. In 1661, 12 years after Charles I had been executed by Cromwell's army, Cromwell's corpse was hanged and beheaded in revenge. The pickled body caused the 'executioners' a problem. What? (Clue: it's a tough job for someone)

30. In 1666 the Great Fire of London swept the city. A Frenchman confessed he started it – even though he couldn't possibly have done. What did the magistrates do with him? (Clue: give him a rise)

31. Many people tried to break out of the Tower of London. But, in 1671, Captain Blood broke in. Why? (Clue: it will be the crowning achievement of his career)

32. In 1685 in Scotland two women were drowned because they refused to say, 'God save ...' who? (Clue: you couldn't say it today either!)

33. In 1688 an Aberdeen Catholic insulted the local Protestants by naming his two dogs after Protestant heroes, Calvin and Luther. What was his punishment? (Clue: it's a dog's life)

34. In 1685 Charles II died. One of his habits had been to take an Egyptian mummy, grind it into a powder and rub the powder into his body. Why? (Clue: power powder)

35. In 1688 in Edinburgh a Mrs Stansfield bought some black clothes that were just right for a widow. What happened two days later? (Clue: did she read her horoscope?)

36. In 1688 unpopular James II was replaced by his daughter, Mary. She celebrated by running into the palace and doing what on the beds? (Clue: she could have hit the ceiling)

37. In Scotland in 1690 John McGilter went to prison for flattening this with a punch. What? (Clue: cart can go before it but *the* cart shouldn't)

38. A guilty Stuart man or woman could

be punished by being stripped and made to walk around the town dressed only in an empty barrel. What was their crime? (Clue: the punishment fits the crime)

39. In Scotland in 1697 a cheeky teenager said, 'Christianity will disappear by 1800.' What did the shocked church ministers do with him? (Clue: will he still be around by 1700?)

40. At the end of the 1690s they were banned and stayed banned till the 1990s. They 'cheat the public' out of their money. What? (Clue: the odds against you winning are only 14 million to one)

Superstar Shakespeare

William Shakespeare used 17,677 different words in his writing. Amazingly, about 1,700 of those were new words! Can you spot the words (or phrases) first used by Shakespeare?

41. A place to stay is. . .
a) accommodation
b) a hotel
c) hard to find

42. If you're puzzled you say. . .
a) it's Greek to me
b) I don't understand
c) eh, you what?

43. If you're not mean you're. . .
a) kind
b) generous
c) sharing your chocolate biscuits

44. If you're unashamed you're. . .
a) open
b) barefaced
c) a nudist

45. To make someone go faster say. . .
a) quicken
b) hurry
c) get on with it

46. A sudden wind is a. . .
a) blast
b) gust
c) little puff

47. A children's game is. . .
a) leapfrog
b) hopscotch
c) hopfrog

48. A reliable person is a. . .
a) tower of strength
b) brick
c) teacher

49. A person with no friends is. . .
a) lonely
b) friendless
c) smelly

50. Something that gets smaller. . .
a) dwindles
b) lessens
c) goes like a jumper in a hot wash

51. An lethal attack on a powerful person is. . .
a) murder
b) assassination
c) a bad idea

Curious cures

Would you make a good Stuart doctor? Match these problems to the right cures . . . just don't expect them to work and don't try them on your friends!

Problem I

52. Accidentally swallowing a snake (!) [Boot it out]
53. Heavy bleeding [This should make it all write]
54. Stopping yourself from becoming drunk [Make a pig of yourself]
55. Colic (stomach pains) [The cure shouldn't kill you stone dead]
56. Toothache [You'll be oak-kay after this]
57. Consumption (lung disease) [This should slip down nicely]
58. Fever [Coo—what a thought]
59. Accidentally swallowing a horse leech in drinking water [Make it flee]
60. Preventing the plague from infecting you [A rich food]
61. Jaundice (liver disease) [wear a clothes peg on your nose]

Cure II

a. Place a cold marble stone (on which the sun has never shone) on the stomach
b. Drink a mixture of fleas and vinegar
c. Eat snails boiled in milk and a few chopped worms if you wish
d. Burn the sole of an old shoe and breath in the smoke
e. Place a gold coin in the mouth
f. Write the word 'Veronica' on your left thumb
g. Take two 'tench' fish, split them open and place them on the feet. Leave for 12 hours 'even if they begin to stink,' then put fresh ones on
h. Cut a pigeon in half and place one half on each foot
i. Scratch your gum with a new nail then drive the nail into an oak tree
j. Eat the roasted lungs of a pig first thing in the morning

Question of the century

62. If April showers bring May flowers, what do May flowers bring?

Remember, remember...

Since the Gunpowder Plot was discovered it has passed into English history and is remembered every 5 November. But how many of these funny Fawkes facts are false?

63. In January 1606 Parliament passed a new law. It said that 5 November would become a holiday of public thanksgiving.

64. Guy Fawkes hasn't always been the one on top of bonfires. At different times in history dummies of different people have been burned on 5 November.

65. It wasn't until 1920 that fireworks were added to the 5 November celebrations.

66. For many years the people of Scotton village in Yorkshire refused to celebrate 5 November with fireworks and bonfires.

67. The government decided that the cellars beneath Parliament should be patrolled night and day to prevent another Gunpowder Plot. That patrol stopped a long time ago.

Out of time

Which of these things were either first popular or invented in Britain in the 1600s?

Test your teacher

How much does your history teacher know about the 1600s? Test them with this quiz – and if they get more than half wrong, threaten them with the Stuart cure for consumption!

78. Why were Oliver Cromwell's followers called 'Roundheads'?
a) because of the shape of their helmets
b) it was an insulting name given to them by the Cavaliers
c) because of their haircuts

79. Which Stuart king was described as 'a nervous drivelling idiot'?
a) James I
b) Charles I
c) James II

80. How did Charles II describe himself?
a) 'the most handsome man in England'
b) 'the King of Elegance'
c) 'an ugly fellow'

81. Who was the leader of the Gunpowder plot?
a) Guy Fawkes
b) Robert Catesby
c) Simon Montfort

82. Prince Rupert, a Cavalier leader during the Civil War, had a dog he took with him everywhere. What breed was it?
a) a black Great Dane
b) an Irish Wolfhound
c) a white Poodle

83. When he was a prince escaping from England (because his father had lost the Civil War), James II dressed as
a) a girl
b) a servant
c) Little Red Riding Hood

84. In the 1600s, who were Stroller's Priests and what did they do?
a) tramps who performed illegal marriages for couples
b) priests who roamed the countryside doing good works
c) thieves who stole from churches

85. What was a 'bung-napper' in Stuart times?
a) a sleep-walker
b) a purse-snatcher
c) a dustman

86. Which of the following was a real 1600s cure for spots?
a) drinking vinegar mixed with chopped-up worms
b) washing in your own pee
c) rubbing in the blood of a freshly killed pigeon

87. Who did Londoners blame for starting the Great Fire of London in 1666?
a) French spies
b) Catholics
c) plague victims

Foreign news

If there had been popular newspapers in the 1600s then these might have been the headlines. Unfortunately some vandal has cut out important words. Can you replace them?

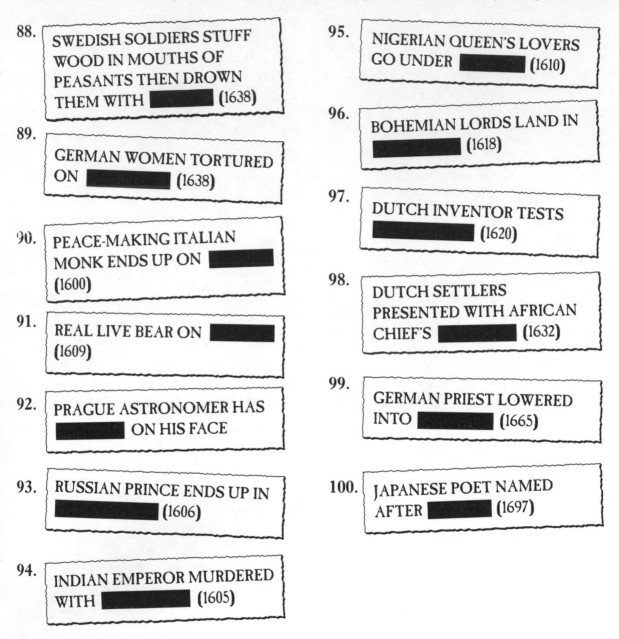

88. SWEDISH SOLDIERS STUFF WOOD IN MOUTHS OF PEASANTS THEN DROWN THEM WITH ▮▮▮▮ (1638)

89. GERMAN WOMEN TORTURED ON ▮▮▮▮ (1638)

90. PEACE-MAKING ITALIAN MONK ENDS UP ON ▮▮▮▮ (1600)

91. REAL LIVE BEAR ON ▮▮▮▮ (1609)

92. PRAGUE ASTRONOMER HAS ▮▮▮▮ ON HIS FACE

93. RUSSIAN PRINCE ENDS UP IN ▮▮▮▮ (1606)

94. INDIAN EMPEROR MURDERED WITH ▮▮▮▮ (1605)

95. NIGERIAN QUEEN'S LOVERS GO UNDER ▮▮▮▮ (1610)

96. BOHEMIAN LORDS LAND IN ▮▮▮▮ (1618)

97. DUTCH INVENTOR TESTS ▮▮▮▮ (1620)

98. DUTCH SETTLERS PRESENTED WITH AFRICAN CHIEF'S ▮▮▮▮ (1632)

99. GERMAN PRIEST LOWERED INTO ▮▮▮▮ (1665)

100. JAPANESE POET NAMED AFTER ▮▮▮▮ (1697)

Words: poison, metal nose, banana, fire, submarine, manure, volcano, head, axe, stage, cannon, rubbish heap, wagon wheels

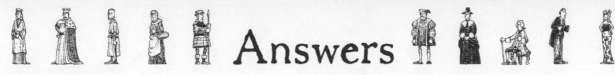

Answers

Quick questions

1. It was meant to cure the fever.
2. She allowed him to be beheaded without being tortured first.
3. Ireland. They failed to meet up with Irish rebel friends and were defeated.
4. She had James's mother, Mary Queen of Scots, beheaded in 1587.
5. Horses. So people can get away from plague-ridden London.
6. He fell off his horse.
7. To protect him from an assassin's knife.
8. His sleeve. He also picked his nose a lot. Would you have wanted to shake hands with him?
9. A pig.
10. Coal. Not the sort of explosive you imagine when you think of Guy Fawkes!
11. Drove them out of town.
12. He had them thrown in prison. Arabella wasn't allowed to marry without the King's permission so she and hubby were both punished. She escaped from the Tower, was recaptured and died in 1615 without ever being freed.
13. He was drowned. This was an old Scottish custom from the days when trees and ropes were too difficult to find.
14. It was a sport in the Cotswold Games. Not as cruel as cock-fighting, hunting hares with hounds, or setting dogs on to chained bears.
15. The cannon was fired as part of the play. Sparks caught the thatched roof and the theatre burned to the ground. The only victim was a man whose trousers caught fire.
16. Women. The writer, Joseph Swetman, suggested the best way to control them was to beat them regularly. Put that stick down at once, boy!
17. He died.
18. Plymouth. They named their new settlement Plymouth Bay because they were too boring to think of an interesting new name – like Disneyland.
19. Bacon caught a cold from being out in the snow. The chicken wasn't too well either.
20. It was burned under the nose of the lawyer. His head was held in a pillory and when the fire died down his ears were cut off. As the knife sliced through the second one he probably muttered, 'Ear we go again.'
21. Corpses. He was used to cutting them up for experiments so he wasn't too bothered about using them as blankets.
22. Golf. A popular game with his family, and granny Mary Queen of Scots enjoyed it too.
23. Charles didn't want to shiver in the cold in case people thought he was shaking with fear.
24. With his own wooden leg.
25. They replaced the corpse with a painted wooden dummy with glass eyes.
26. As a salt cellar.
27. Tobacco. Culpepper even said tobacco ash was good for cleaning the teeth! Ugh!
28. He sat up and hit the man who was cutting him open! That took guts!
29. The corpse was pickled and had gone very hard. It took the axeman eight chops to cut through the tough neck. Cromwell didn't complain.
30. They hanged him anyway.
31. He stole the crown jewels. He was soon caught yet curiously King Charles forgave the rogue.
32. The King. It was against their religion to say 'God Save the King' when they were ordered to. They were tied to a stake at the mouth of a river and made to watch as the tide came in.
33. The poor dogs were arrested and hanged at the Market Cross!
34. He believed the greatness of the Egyptian kings would rub off on to him.
35. Her husband died! Her actions were so suspicious that she was accused of murder.
36. It's said she bounced on the palace beds for joy at her father's defeat in the 'Glorious revolution'.
37. A horse. He was drunk at the time ... McGilter, not the horse, you fool.
38. Being drunk. The barrel was known as a 'Drunkard's Cloak' and could be a wine barrel or one for draught beer. A bit draughty in winter.
39. He was executed. The boy pleaded that he'd been young and foolish. It didn't save his neck.
40. Lotteries.

Superstar Shakespeare

41.a) 42.a) 43.b) 44.b) 45.b) 46.b) 47.a) 48.a) 49.a) 50.a) 51.b)

Anyone who answered c) has a brain like Shakespeare's! (Dead for 400 years.)

Curious cures
52.d) 53.f) 54.j) 55.a) 56.i) 57.c) 58.h) 59.b) 60.e) 61.g)

Question of the century
62. Pilgrim Fathers.

Remember, remember...
63. True. People lit bonfires to celebrate and threw dummies on the fire dressed as Guy Fawkes.
64. True. The first record of this was at Cliffe Hill in London 1606 where a dummy of the Pope joined Guy Fawkes in the flames.
65. False. Within a few years of the plot people began to use fireworks on November 5.
66. True. This village was where Guy Fawkes used to live and the people didn't think it was fair that Guy should take all the blame.
67 . False. A search of the cellars is still carried out before the opening of every Parliament.

Out of time
68. Horse-drawn fire-engine – Yes. London, 1625.
69. Eating with forks – Yes. Forks had been used on royal tables as early as the 14th century but only became popular when Thomas Coryat published a book about their use in Italy.
70. Pineapples – Yes. In 1657 Oliver Cromwell was presented with the first pineapple in Britain.
71. Sandwiches – No. British politician, John Montagu, 4th Earl of Sandwich, had a habit of eating beef between slices of toast so he could play cards and eat at the same time. He gave his name to this type of food in the 1700s but the Romans first had the idea of eating meat between bread.
72. Coffee – Yes. Coffee was a popular Arab drink for hundreds of years but the Brits only discovered it in the middle of the 17th century.
73. Bananas – Yes. Thomas Johnson showed bananas in his London shop window in 1633.
74. Tea – Yes. People of the 17th century thought it was fine to drink tea from the saucer.
75. Drinking chocolate – Yes. The Spanish brought chocolate back from Mexico in 1519, but it first became popular in Stuart Britain. It was rather greasy, and sometimes the dealers added soil to the cocoa paste to cheat the buyers.

76. Eating chocolate – No. The Dutch first made chocolate for eating in 1828.
77. Cabbage – No. Blame the Tudors for that. Sir Anthony Ashley of Dorset brought cabbages to Britain from Holland.

Test your teacher
78.c) 79.a) 80.c) 81.b) 82.c) 83.a) 84.a) 85.b) 86.c) 87.a)

Foreign news
88. Manure. From the Thirty Years War in Northern Europe.
89. Wagon wheels. Also from the Thirty Years War. Women were tied to the wheels and the wagons set off.
90. Fire. Italian Bruno wanted to make peace between Catholics and Protestants. The Catholics burned him.
91. Stage. William Shakespeare used a bear in his production of *The Winter's Tale*.
92. Metal nose. Tycho Brahe lost his nose in a sword fight and had it replaced with a metal one.
93. Cannon. Dmitri's killers weren't satisfied with burning his corpse. They put the ashes in a cannon and blasted them away.
94. Poison. No one knows who did it. Akbar was so unpopular there were hundreds of suspects!
95. Axe. Queen Amina found a new boyfriend in every city she captured – then had them beheaded!
96. Rubbish heap. When the lords were attacked in their castle they jumped out of the windows. The rubbish broke their fall and they survived.
97. Submarine. He tried out his underwater rowing boat on the River Thames. It sank.
98. Head. The Dutch settlers complained about a theft, and the chief's head was given to them as a way of saying, 'Sorry'.
99. Volcano. Kircher was a scientist and explored Vesuvius for himself. He survived.
100. Banana. Basho was Japan's greatest poet of the 1600s – in spite of having a name that meant 'banana tree'!

The 1700s
The gorgeous Georgians

This was the age when pirates were the scourge of the seas, highwaymen haunted the roads, a crackpot was king and the Americans were revolting . . . some things never change. It was also the age of thick make-up, beauty spots, monstrous wigs and padded bosoms – and that was just the men.

Quick questions

1. In 1700 John Asgill went to prison for writing a short book called, *A man can go from here to heaven without. . .* Without what? (Clue: everybody does it)

2. In Scotland in 1700 a teacher was whipped through the streets of Edinburgh (don't laugh!). What was his crime? (Clue: tough teacher)

3. In 1707 the son of the Duke of Queensberry murdered a kitchen boy. How did he dispose of the evidence? (Clue: it's in really bad taste)

4. Why did Queen Anne's doctors shave her head and cover her feet in garlic? (Clue: sick idea)

5. Queen Anne died in 1714 and she was buried in a coffin that is almost square. Why? (Clue: if the coffin fits, wear it)

6. German George I took the throne. But where was his wife Dorothea? (Clue: she flirted once too often)

7. In Banff in 1714 the town hangman had to catch stray dogs. He was paid for each dog he caught. How did he prove he'd caught a dog? (Clue: hide!)

8. In 1717 a Scottish teacher murdered two pupils in his charge. Before he was hanged he had an odd punishment. What was it? (Clue: he'd never write on a blackboard again)

9. In 1718 the dreaded pirate Blackbeard was shot and beheaded by a navy officer. Blackbeard's body was thrown over the side of the ship. What's supposed to have happened next? (Clue: maybe he crawled)

10. Many Georgian pirates wore gold earrings. Why? (Clue: go to see?)

11. In 1722 an elephant died on its way to Dundee. What did Doctor Patrick Blair do with the corpse? (Clue: jumbo scientist)

12. In 1724 murderer Maggie Dickson escaped execution. The law said she couldn't be hanged. Why? (Clue: second time lucky)

13. In 1727 George I's hated wife, Dorothea, died. He set off for the funeral but failed to get there. Why? (Clue: a second funeral delayed him)

14. Soon after George I died a raven flew in at the window of his girlfriend, the Duchess of Kendal. She looked after it better than any pet. Why? (Clue: it was something George had crowed about)

15. In 1739 the famous highwayman, Dick Turpin, was executed. His handwriting was recognized by someone who knew him at school and he was betrayed. Who betrayed Turpin? (Clue: master of treachery)

16. How can a hot poker cure toothache? (Clue: ear we go again)

17. George II and his family ate Sunday dinner in style. What could the public buy on those Sundays? (Clue: feeding time at the zoo?)

18. In the sport of 'Goose Riding' a live goose was hung from a tree branch by its feet. The competitor climbed on a horse. What did he have to do to win? (Clue: the best rider would win by a neck)

19. In 1743 George II became the last British monarch to lead an army into battle at Dettingen, Germany. But his horse disgraced him. How? (Clue: might have made a good race horse)

20. In 1746 James Reid played his bagpipes in York. He never played them again. Why not? (Clue: the noise he made was criminal)

21. In 1747 Lord Lovat became the last person to be beheaded in the Tower of London. As he went to his death 20 other innocent people died. How? (Clue: curiosity killed the cat)

22. In 1748 George II's oldest son, Prince Frederick, was hit with a tennis ball in the stomach. How did it affect him in 1751? (Clue: we've never had a King Fred)

23. A gang of smugglers cought a law officer and left him for dead after teaching him not to be too nosey. What did they do? (Clue: how did he smell?)

24. In 1755 an old man was buried at a crossroads in Cornwall with a stake through his heart. What had he done? (Clue: he brought it on himself)

25. Georgians ate cooked tomatoes but never raw tomatoes. Why not? (Clue: doctor's orders)

26. At a 1758 fair one of the attractions was a man eating a chicken. What was so unusual about this? (Clue: it took guts)

27. In 1758 Georgians started using bank notes as well as coins. This was followed by a new crime. What? (Clue: copy-cats)

28. When George III came to the throne in 1760 the cruel crowds cried 'Pug!' at the queen. Why? (Clue: not puppy love)

29. What would a Georgian lady do with a dead mouse? (Clue: modern women use a pencil instead)

30. In 1762 a sheep thief tied the back legs of a sheep together and threw the rope around his neck to help him carry it. He hanged for his theft . . . but in a weird way. How? (Clue: the sheep's revenge?)

31. In 1770 Captain James Cook claimed a new country for England. The natives objected and threatened him with a weapon the Brits had never seen before. What? (Clue: the answer will come back to you)

32. In 1773 Americans rebelled against British taxes on things like tea. What did they do with tea chests arriving in British ships? (Clue: a new way to make tea?)

33. In 1776 a lady wore a hat at a picnic, which had decorative fruit and vegetables pinned to it. A cow ate the hat. What happened next? (Clue: how do you turn a cow to beef?)

34. In 1788 an Edinburgh councillor, Deacon Brodie, invented a hanging machine with a trapdoor. How did the Deacon prove that it worked? (Clue: first hand experience)

35. Posh Georgian ladies wore tight iron belts to give them amazingly thin waists. Elizabeth Evelyn's belt killed her, which was especially sad. Why? (Clue: too small to begin with)

36. In 1790 a sailor disguised himself as a woman to avoid being forced to join the navy. The navy spotted his disguise and took him anyway. How did they spot him? (Clue: it should have been a close shave)

37. 'Women fainted at the sight, children screamed and dogs yelped,' in the 1790s. What did men start wearing that caused this sensation? (Clue: get ahead, get a hat)

38. King George III suffered periods of mental illness. During one attack he dressed in black in memory of, 'That good man,' whom he believed to be dead. Who? (Clue: if George had been well he'd have known the man was alive)

39. In 1797 the rebellious pupils at Rugby public school decided to break into the headmaster's room. What did they use to get through the thick door? (Clue: it wasn't even the fifth of November)

40. Why did Georgian dentists buy tusks of hippo and walrus? (Clue: fangs very much)

Foul for females

What was it like for Georgian women? Try this simple test –
answer true or false. . .

41. Georgian women put cork balls in
their cheeks to improve their appearance.

42. The average age for women to get
married was 15.

43. A woman could be burned alive for
murdering her husband.

44. Georgian wives were sometimes sold
by their husbands at auction.

45. Men were allowed to beat their wives
with sticks.

46. Ladies used
cement as make-up.

47. The average
wage for a maid was
£3 a month.

48. Georgian women often took snuff.

49. A group of Welsh women stopped an
invasion by the French.

50. It was fashionable for women to have
a sun tan.

Out of time

Can you spot which of these things were first seen in 1700s Britain?

Test your teacher

Teachers love asking questions. They even get *paid* for it! Now it's your chance to get your revenge. Test your teacher (or pester your parent) with this amazingly difficult quiz. When they get a wrong answer you can mutter, 'I thought you'd have known that!'

62. What did a Georgian doctor use to pull out rotten teeth?
a) a penguin
b) a pelican
c) a puffin

63. In 1750 a gentleman fed a dish of smuggled tea to what?
a) a dog
b) a cat
c) a rat

64. Where did Robinson Cruso live?
a) King's Lynn, Norfolk
b) on a desert island
c) in a deserted Ireland

65. In 1774 a Huntingdon highwayman held up a coach using what?
a) a walking stick
b) a candlestick
c) a bag of sick

66. Georgian gentlemen in Britain would not wear what?
a) flared trousers
b) pink trousers
c) any trousers

67. What did sailors use their stale cheese supplies for?
a) carved it into buttons
b) fed it to rats and the rats broke their teeth and starved to death
c) grated it and stuffed their mattresses with it

68. Carlisle Spedding invented a 'steel mill' – it struck sparks off a flintstone and gave light. Useful for pitmen in a coal mine. How did Spedding die?
a) he trapped a finger in his steel mill and it turned poisonous
b) his steel mill caused an explosion of gas in a coal mine
c) a dissatisfied miner smashed the steel mill over Spedding's head

69. What did some racist Georgians do to foreigners on the streets of London?
a) threw books entitled 'Learn yourself English' at them
b) threw Scotsmen at them
c) threw dead cats and dogs at them

70. What useful thing did the watch-maker Andrew Cumming invent in 1775 that we still use today?
a) a think-tank
b) a chin-strap
c) a stink-trap

71. The Georgians enjoyed watching hounds tearing hares apart. But when was the sport stopped?
a) when the hare waved a white flag
b) when Queen Victoria was splattered with hare blood in 1899
c) never

IF THEIR DOG GOT TORN UP, WOULD THEY STILL ENJOY IT?

Foreign affairs

Sometimes letters from abroad are opened and read by a government 'censor'. He cuts out unsuitable words or phrases. That's what happened to these letters. Can you guess what's missing?

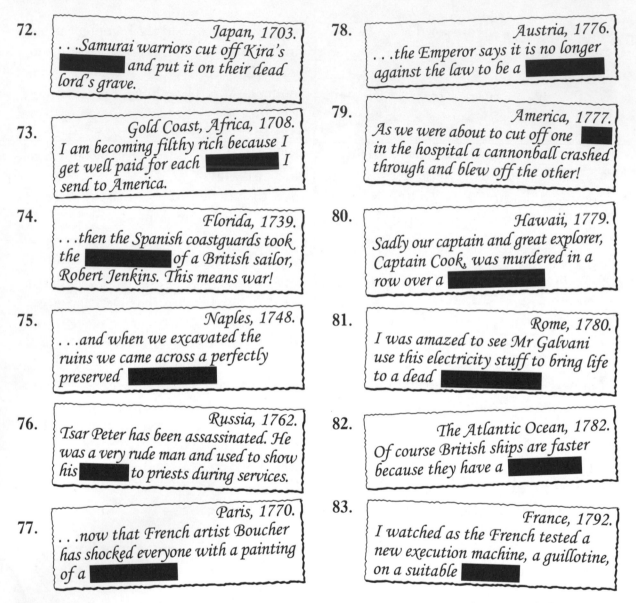

72. *Japan, 1703.*
. . .Samurai warriors cut off Kira's ▆▆▆▆▆ and put it on their dead lord's grave.

73. *Gold Coast, Africa, 1708.*
I am becoming filthy rich because I get well paid for each ▆▆▆▆▆ I send to America.

74. *Florida, 1739.*
. . .then the Spanish coastguards took the ▆▆▆▆▆ of a British sailor, Robert Jenkins. This means war!

75. *Naples, 1748.*
. . .and when we excavated the ruins we came across a perfectly preserved ▆▆▆▆▆

76. *Russia, 1762.*
Tsar Peter has been assassinated. He was a very rude man and used to show his ▆▆▆▆▆ to priests during services.

77. *Paris, 1770.*
. . .now that French artist Boucher has shocked everyone with a painting of a ▆▆▆▆▆

78. *Austria, 1776.*
. . .the Emperor says it is no longer against the law to be a ▆▆▆▆▆

79. *America, 1777.*
As we were about to cut off one ▆▆▆▆▆ in the hospital a cannonball crashed through and blew off the other!

80. *Hawaii, 1779.*
Sadly our captain and great explorer, Captain Cook, was murdered in a row over a ▆▆▆▆▆

81. *Rome, 1780.*
I was amazed to see Mr Galvani use this electricity stuff to bring life to a dead ▆▆▆▆▆

82. *The Atlantic Ocean, 1782.*
Of course British ships are faster because they have a ▆▆▆▆▆

83. *France, 1792.*
I watched as the French tested a new execution machine, a guillotine, on a suitable ▆▆▆▆▆

Words: tongue, naked woman, frog, leg, witch, slave, corpse, copper bottom, skeleton, ear, boat, head

Question of the century
84. Where did the French revolutionaries buy their guillotines?

Chop and change

The French Revolution was famous for its automatic neck-chopper, the guillotine. But which of the following foul facts are true? Answer in French, s'il vous plait. 'Oui' for yes or 'Non' for no. Queen Marie Antoinette's wigs for winners – a pain in the neck for losers.
Oui or non...?

85. The man who designed the French version of the guillotine was Doctor Joseph-Ignace Guillotin.

86. The chopping machine wasn't always called a guillotine. At first it was named a Louisette. Criminals later nicknamed it 'The Widow'.

87. The guillotine's designer said that all the victim felt was a chill on the back of the neck.

88. There was a rule that said French women should be taught about the Revolution. They were encouraged to take their knitting to the executions and watch.

89. One woman who cashed in on the executions was Madame Marie Tussaud. She made 'death masks' of the famous heads and took them fresh from the guillotine basket.

90. The people of Lyon suffered mass guillotine sessions because few people there had supported the Revolution. The guillotine couldn't get through the necks quickly enough in the city of Lyon so the revolutionaries brought in good old firing squads to help kill more.

Wacky words

Can you match the following Georgian words to their meanings. . .?

91. grunter	a) idiot
92. hock–docky	b) hangman's noose
93. sumph	c) police constable
94. scrag	d) horse
95. bolly dog	e) shoe
96. big bug	f) eye
97. squeezer	g) shilling coin
98. sad man	h) neck
99. daisy-kicker	i) trouble-maker
100. killer	j) important man

Answers

Quick questions

1. Dying. The booklet was burned, so we'll never know how to do this clever trick!

2. He had flogged a pupil until the pupil died. And there are still people today who want to bring back beatings for children. Avoid them.

3. He roasted the boy and ate him. Do not try this with your school dinner ladies, please.

4. They were trying to cure her illness. They also blistered her skin with hot irons and gave her medicines to make her vomit. She died – and was probably glad to go.

5. Anne was so fat she was almost square.

6. She was locked away back in Germany. This was her punishment for flirting with Count Konigsmark. It was worse for the count. He'd been murdered and secretly buried at the castle. Jolly George.

7. He collected the skins of the dogs. He was probably happy to do this because one of his other jobs was to sweep up doggy poo from the streets!

8. He had both hands chopped off.

9. It's said Blackbeard's headless corpse swam round the ship three times before finally sinking!

10. They believed it helped their eyesight.

11. He cut it open to see how an elephant's body works.

12. Because she had been hanged once and pronounced dead. As she was taken off to the graveyard in her coffin she sat up! Lucky Maggie lived another 30 years before dying a second time – for good.

13. George died on his way to the funeral. He had held up Dorothea's funeral for six months. If he'd been quicker he'd have had the pleasure of seeing her put six feet under.

14. George had said that he would visit her after his death. She believed the raven was George. Caw! Imagine that!

15. Turpin's school master betrayed him.

16. Burning a hole through the lobe of your ear was supposed to cure the pain in the tooth. Crazy! If you ever see your dentist with a hot poker you know it's time to change dentists.

17. The public could buy tickets to watch George II and the royal family dine. You could try selling tickets for your neighbours to watch you eat your beans on toast!

18. Grab the head of the goose and tear it off. This was made harder by greasing the goose's beak.

19. As soon as it heard enemy gunfire it ran away. George couldn't stop it! The fat little feller had to go back to his command on foot.

20. He was hanged. The bagpipes were declared 'an instrument of war' after the Scottish Jacobite rebellion of 1745. Happily it is now legal to play these beautiful melodic instruments.

21. Spectators crowded on to wooden stands to watch Lovat get lopped. The stands collapsed and killed 20 people. Served them right.

22. It killed him. In 1751 he caught a chill but it was the stomach damage, caused by the ball, that finished him off.

23. They cut off his nose. They then dumped him down a well but two days later he was still alive. They threw logs down the well to finish him off. After that he didn't feel too well.

24. He had committed suicide. A suicide's spirit was supposed to haunt the earth. By burying him at a cross-roads he wouldn't know which way to turn so he'd have to stay there. The stake through the heart helped.

25. They believed that raw fruits caused the plague.

26. He ate the whole chicken – guts, feathers and all – and it was alive. At least it was when he started eating.

27. Banknote forgery. Richard Vaughan had the honour of being the first man to be hanged for copying the notes. Now you know why your teachers tell you not to copy!

28. They thought her upturned nose made her look just like a pug dog. The German queen didn't understand and thought they were shouting 'God save the Queen'!

29. Mouse skin was used to make false eyebrows.

30. The sheep struggled and pulled the rope tight around the thief's neck. He was strangled – the sheep lived, you'll be pleased to hear. A lesson for all ram-raiders.

31. Boomerangs. The country is Australia.

32. They dumped the tea into the harbour. Many rebels at the 'Boston Tea Party' were disguised as

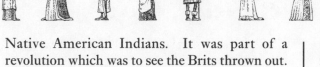

Native American Indians. It was part of a revolution which was to see the Brits thrown out.

33. The cow choked on a pin and died. And the hills were alive with the sound of moo-sick.

34. Brodie was the first man to be executed on the machine. He was a councillor by day but a burglar by night.

35. Elizabeth was just two years old when she died. At least skinny Lizzie would have fitted in her pram.

36. He was wearing a beard. Silly, but true.

37. Top hats.

38. George III was sure poor George III was dead. His mental illness was sad. The treatments his doctors gave him were really mad. One was to shout at the king while his mouth was stuffed with handkerchiefs so he couldn't shout back.

39. Gunpowder. Boom! Boom!

40. They use them to make false teeth for human patients.

Foul for females

41. True.

42. False. The average age was about 24. Very few married under 16.

43. True. But this law was changed in 1789 and the punishment was changed to hanging.

44. True. It wasn't legal but it sometimes happened – and continued to happen until 1887.

45. True. But the stick he used had to be no thicker than his thumb, so that's all right.

46. False. But they did use lead paint, arsenic powder and plaster of Paris.

47. False. They would be paid about £3 a year.

48. True.

49. True. In 1797 a small group of women from Pembrokeshire, led by Jemima Nicholas, captured 20 men from the invading French. They were so terrifying that the French army surrendered.

50. False. A pale skin was beautiful to the Georgians and women would sometimes wear a mask in front of the face to protect the skin.

Out of time

51. Steam engine – No. The first recorded one was in 1698. The 1700s did see the first steam powered vehicle though.

52. Piano – Yes. First in Britain in 1711, brought from Rome.

53. Bathroom with hot and cold running water – Yes. In 1701 at Chatsworth, Derbyshire.

54. Police detective – No. First appeared in France in 1812. Though there were policemen called Bow Street Runners by 1749 in London.

55. Roller skates – Yes. Worn by Joseph Merlin to a musical party in 1760. He skated into the ballroom, playing a violin. Sadly he lost control, skated into a £500 mirror, smashed it, smashed his violin and almost cut himself to shreds.

56. Jigsaw puzzle – Yes. First seen in 1763. The oldest surviving one is a 1767 map of England where you have to fit the counties in the right place. Very educational.

57. Sewing machine – Yes. First seen in London in 1790. Designed to sew leather boots and shoes.

58. Post Office letter box – No. First seen in Britain in 1809, but the first red pillar box didn't appear until 1852. Before the first letter box a man walked round the streets ringing a bell.

59. Railway bridge – Yes. Causey Arch, County Durham was built in 1727 ... even though steam trains weren't invented! The wooden railway carried horse-drawn coal trucks.

60. Iron boat – Yes. John Wilkinson built a 20-metre barge in 1787, not the first iron ship but by far the biggest.

61. Tinned food – No. Introduced to Britain in 1812. The French came up with the idea in 1795 but used glass bottles.

Test your teacher

62.b) A 'pelican' was a tool for pulling out difficult teeth. The instrument got its name because it looked like a pelican's beak.

63.a) The dog died. Smuggled tea wasn't always as pure as the stuff you get in your tea bags.

64.a) Robinson Cruso, a bed-maker, lived in King's Lynn High Street. The writer Daniel Defoe visited King's Lynn on his travels and must have seen the name Robinson Cruso outside the shop, because he called his famous book *Robinson Crusoe*.

65.b) The highwayman couldn't afford a pistol. The guard wasn't fooled and shot the robber dead.

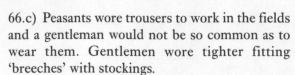

66.c) Peasants wore trousers to work in the fields and a gentleman would not be so common as to wear them. Gentlemen wore tighter fitting 'breeches' with stockings.

67.a) And the biscuits were often worse than the cheese – full of black-headed maggots.

68.b) When it was used in a mine it could explode 'fire damp' gas. It killed a lot of miners. Spedding went speeding to his death when he tested it.

69.c)

70.c) A 'stink-trap' is a bend in the toilet pipe that stops smells coming up from the drains. Very useful. Your toilet has this useful bend, so don't try to straighten it.

71.c) That's right. Hare 'coursing' as it's called is still enjoyed today by many people and many packs of hounds. That's life, hare today, gone tomorrow.

Foreign affairs

72. Head. After taking their revenge, the Samurai warriors killed themselves so they could join their lord in death.

73. Slave. Tens of thousands of Africans were snatched from their villages and transported to be slaves in America.

74. Ear. Jenkins refused to pay Spanish customs tax. The Spanish sliced off his ear and told him to take it back to his king. He did! The fighting that followed became known as 'The War of Jenkins's Ear'. (Just as well they didn't cut a slice off his bum!)

75. Skeleton. King Charles III ordered workers to dig under the volcanic ash of Vesuvius. They found the well preserved ruins of Pompeii where bodies were 'frozen' as they died in AD 79.

76. Tongue. Peter died in a scuffle and his bodyguard said he couldn't remember what happened. This is a very useful story if you ever find yourself in trouble!

77. Naked woman. The paintings were very popular but mostly with men for some reason.

78. Witch. The Emperor also banned tortures such as the rack but he kept flogging and branding. Kind man.

79. Leg. The unfortunate British soldier was about to have his leg amputated when a stray cannonball blew off the other and killed him before he could hop off the operating table.

80. Boat. A Hawaiian chief 'borrowed' Captain Cook's boat so Cook led an attack of sailors with guns against Hawaiians with spears. The Hawaiians weren't afraid of the guns because they'd never seen them before. Cook was killed.

81. Frog. Galvani was working with 'static' electricity and noticed the effect of the charge on a dead frog, they say. But what was a dead frog doing in his lab?

82. Copper bottom. It stopped the weeds and barnacles clinging to the hull and slowing the ship down. (Please note: 'Copper bottom' is not the answer to no. 76!)

83. Corpse. The French tested the guillotine on dead bodies from a local hospital before using it on a live highwayman. When the French Revolution started in 1793 the guillotine was used on tens of thousands, faster than a chip-shop chipper.

Question of the century
84. In the chopping centre

Chop and change
85–90. ALL are true. That's a lot of ouis.

Wacky words
91.g) 92.e) 93.a) 94.h) 95.c) 96.j) 97.b) 98.i) 99.d) 100.f)

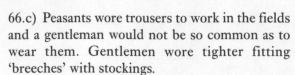

The 1800s
The vile Victorians

This was the age of Charles Dickens and chubby little Queen Victoria, of horrible historical slums, of vile Victorian villains, gloomy factories and deep, dark, deadly mines. Not to mention school for everyone, and Jack the Ripper... You might ask, 'Which is worse?'

Quick questions

1. How old were the youngest chimney sweeps in 1804? (Clue: not infants)

2. How was Lord Nelson's body brought home after his death at Trafalgar in 1805? (Clue: not a barrel of laughs)

3. John Bellingham blamed the government for ruining his business. How did he get his revenge in 1812? (Clue: a blow to the head)

4. Napoleon lost the Battle of Waterloo in 1815. What did Brit General Lord Raglan lose? (Clue: 'armless sort of chap)

5. In 1817 Brixton prison invented a new punishment for criminals. What? (Clue: hamster toy)

6. In 1818 Mary Shelley wrote a horrific story that is still popular today. What is it called? (Clue: frankly monstrous)

7. In 1820 in Scotland a rebel weaver was the last man to be sentenced to an ancient punishment. What? (Clue: long and drawn out)

8. In 1821 Queen Caroline died. What did this odd queen put on her head to keep cool while she was out riding? (Clue: American pie)

9. In 1822 King George IV visited Scotland and wore a kilt. How did he keep his knees warm? (Clue: they weren't loose)

10. In 1823 a boy at a public school, William Webb Ellis, cheated at football and invented a new game. What? (Clue: you have to hand it to him)

11. In Edinburgh in 1828 William Burke was accused of 16 murders. What did he do with the bodies? (Clue: they were a little cut up about it)

12. In 1830 the Liverpool to Manchester railway opened. How did Liverpool MP William Huskisson celebrate? (Clue: it's a knockout)

13. In 1831 the north-eastern port of Sunderland brought in a new import. What? (Clue: dis eez a horrible thing to suffer)

14. In 1842 women were banned from doing something they had been doing for hundreds of years. What? (Clue: mine, all mine!)

15. In 1844 a lady wrote that people were pleased when they smelled bad drains. Why? (Clue: red sky at night)

16. In 1846 a 16-year-old boy was charged with travelling on a train on a 12-year-old's half-price ticket. What was his excuse? (Clue: time to grow)

17. London 'toshers' waded though sewage every day – up to 1.5 metres of the stuff. Why? (Clue: a golden opportunity)

18. In 1847 the Irish were crowding on to 'coffin ships'. Why? (Clue: they've had their chips)

19. In 1848 many European countries were in revolt. The British rebels, the Chartists, had a rally in London but it was a failure. Why? (Clue: it's a wash out)

20. In 1852 in London a small room is opened for men in Fleet Street and they are very relieved! Why? (Clue: gents still use them)

21. In 1853, Australia got stroppy and refused to take any more from Britain. What? (Clue: if they're barred from Australia they'll be barred in Britain)

22. In 1855 Florence Nightingale was nursing Brit soldiers who were fighting the Russians. What happened to their amputated limbs? (Clue: it will make you pig sick)

23. Punching opponents and gouging their eyes was banned in which sport in 1863? (Clue: players put their foot in it)

24. Irish rebels in 1866 invaded which British territory? (Clue: they mountied a successful defence)

25. In 1869 sailors were banned from wearing what? (Clue: it's a close shave)

26. When this man died in 1870 it was said he was 'exhausted by fame'. Who was he? (Clue: no more Christmas Carols)

27. In 1870 a new law forced everyone to do it, even poor little children. What? (Clue: you had to join the class war)

28. In 1871 explorer Henry Stanley found a famous Scot missionary in the heart of Africa. Everyone knows he said, 'Doctor Livingstone, I presume.' But what was the Doctor's one-word reply? (Clue: that's right!)

29. In 1879 the Tay Bridge collapsed and a train with almost 100 passengers sank. The bridge inspector had said it was safe. How many bridges had he inspected before? (Clue: not enough)

30. In 1880 the famous writer George Eliot died. What's unusual about him? (Clue: he isn't)

31. SS *Daphne* was launched on the river Clyde and the workers got a huge surprise. What? (Clue: duck!)

32. General Gordon was killed defending Khartoum in the Sudan in 1885. They say he went to battle with a cane in one hand and what in the other? (Clue: God help him!)

33. In 1888 the police named a murderer even though they never caught him (or her). Who? (Clue: and Jill?)

34. In 1890 a man died. He had been cruelly put on show to the ghoulish public because of his unusual illness. It made him look like what? (Clue: big ears)

35. Copy-cat Blackpool built a copy of the Eiffel Tower in 1894. But is the Blackpool Tower bigger or smaller than the French one? (Clue: it's one or the other!)

36. In 1896 Londoners saw 'Boxing Kangaroos' in Australia. How? (Clue: somebody shot the kangaroos)

37. In 1896 motorists were glad to see the back of a rule that slowed them down. What rule? (Clue: they weren't glad to see the back of this man)

38. In 1899 Percy Pilcher fell 10 metres and was killed. What did he fall from? (Clue: he was hanging around)

39. Queen Victoria's son-in-law, Prince Christian, lost an eye in a shooting accident. At dinner parties he entertained guests with his collection of what? (Clue: quite a sight)

40. During the Second Boer War in South Africa, what did Victoria order to be sent to each of her 'dear, brave soldiers'? (Clue: very sweet of her)

Question of the century
41. What have William the Fourth and Popeye the Sailor got in common?

Umms and Errs

The 1800s were the age of the melodrama. Before the days of television the century's soap operas took place in thrilling theatres where villainous Victorians battled against hapless heroes. You just *know* what they are going to say . . . or do you?

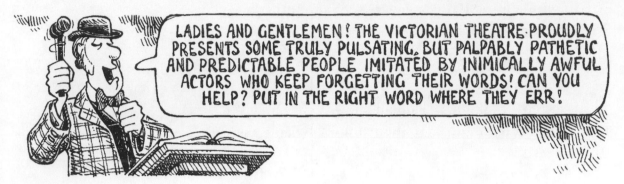

LADIES AND GENTLEMEN! THE VICTORIAN THEATRE PROUDLY PRESENTS SOME TRULY PULSATING, BUT PALPABLY PATHETIC AND PREDICTABLE PEOPLE IMITATED BY INIMICALLY AWFUL ACTORS WHO KEEP FORGETTING THEIR WORDS! CAN YOU HELP? PUT IN THE RIGHT WORD WHERE THEY ERR!

42. East Lynne
Poor Isabel leaves her husband but sneaks back (disguised as a governess) to nurse her sickly son. He dies in her arms as Isabel cries...

Oh, Willie, my child! Dead! Dead! Dead! And never called me errrr!

43. Youth
A bunch of English soldiers struggle against the enemy who must be evil because they aren't English. (The Victorians could be nasty racists.) Their colonel encourages them...

Remember, Great England is looking at you! Show how her sons can fight and errr!

44. The Fatal Marriage
Poor Isabella loses her husband and marries a dear friend. Then her first husband returns. She tries to murder him then decides to stab herself instead. (Don't try this at home.) Isabella sobs...

When I am dead, forgive me and errr me!

45. The Harp of Altenberg
Our heroine, Innogen, is captured by the villain, Brenno. As she tries to escape he grabs hold of her and Innogen cries...

Errrr me!

46. Sweeney Todd or, The Barber of Fleet Street
Sweeney Todd the Barber cuts the throats of customers and drops the corpses into his cellar. There his next-door neighbour collects the bodies and chops them up to make meat pies. As Sweeney cuts a throat he cries...

I errrr them off!

47. Maria Marten or, Murder in the Red Barn
Based on a true 1827 murder. William Corder waits in the barn for sweet Maria but plans to shoot her. Corder sneers...

I now await my victim. Will she come? Yes, for women are foolish enough to do anything for the men they errrr!

Behave like a Victorian

If a time machine dropped your dad in Victorian London would he act like a gentleman . . . or a slob? Test him with these 'do' and 'don't' problems taken from a book of Gentlemen's Manners and see if he could have been accepted by polite Victorians. Just one problem . . . if he makes a single mistake he could well be frowned on for the rest of his life!

Do or don't...
48. offer your hand to an older person to be shaken.
49. eat from the side of your soup spoon and not the end.
50. write to people you know on post cards.
51. remove your overcoat before you enter someone's living room.
52. use slang words.
53. bite into your bread at dinner.
54. call your servants 'girls'.
55. raise your hat to a lady in the street.
56. spit on the pavement.
57. sit with legs crossed.

Manchester misery

58. Not many men in Victorian England were gentlemen – which was unfortunate because gentlemen lived longer than working men. If you were an upper class person living in Manchester in 1842 you could expect to live 38 years (on average). But, if you were in the working class what was the average you could expect to live?
a) 37 years
b) 27 years
c) 17 years

Trasseno talk

'Trasseno' was a name for Victorian villains. They had their own way of life in the slums, and they also had their own language. What would you say to a Trasseno if he (or she) said these things to you? Would you answer 'Yes' or 'No'? Be careful! Give the wrong answer to some and something very nasty could happen...

59. 'Do you fancy a chat?'
60. 'Would you like me to nail your broken door?'
61. 'Shall I give you this finny?'
62. 'Do you think teachers should give their pupils dewskitches?'
63. 'Want a ride on my flummut horse?'
64. 'Would you like to put a jack under the wheel of my carriage?'

65. 'Are you flat?'
66. 'Is your father a nammo?'
67. 'Shall I invite some jolly people to your party?'
68. 'Do you wear a flag when you are cooking?'

Odd one out

The Victorians were great inventors. There are fifteen inventions in this picture . . . but only ten were first produced between 1800 and 1900, anywhere in the world. Can you spot the odd ones out and the odd ones in?

Name that kid

Parents sometimes gave their children curious names, and the Victorians were no different. Which of the following are real Victorian first names and which are not?

- 84. YETTY
- 85. BRAINED
- 86. QUINCE
- 87. POMEGRANATE
- 88. DESPAIR
- 89. GAZZA
- 90. MURDER
- 91. VENUS
- 92. FEATHER
- 93. STARKEY

Howzat Victoria?

The English lost a cricket match against Australia for the first time in 1880. They burned a bail to ashes and have played for those Ashes ever since. 'How's that?' the cricketers cried (or 'Howzat?' in cricket language) when they thought a batsman was out. And 'Howzat?' is the question about these curious Queen Victoria facts.

94. She was the shortest *and* the longest reigning monarch Britain ever had! Howzat?

95. Victoria was responsible for the death of her beloved husband, Albert. Howzat?

96. The police set Victoria up as the target for a murdering gunman. Howzat?

97. Victoria was highly respectable all her life yet she caused a scandal in her coffin. Howzat?

98. Albert and Victoria were married in 1840 though he never proposed to her. Howzat?

99. The Victorians liked portrait paintings but she preferred a particular kind. Howzat?

100. Victoria was Queen of England yet the 'Queen's English' was never very good. Howzat?

Answers

Quick questions

1. Four years old. The sweeps weren't supposed to be under nine but employers lied about the ages of their workers.

2. Pickled in a barrel of brandy. It preserved the body – and the sailors drank the brandy afterwards!

3. He shot the Prime Minister, Spencer Perceval, dead. The only Brit PM to be assassinated. Bellingham was hanged.

4. His arm. He also almost lost his wedding ring when the arm was amputated. 'Here! Bring that arm back!' he cried from his hospital bed.

5. The 'treadmill' – a bit like a hamster wheel, where the prisoners walk and walk and go nowhere.

6. *Frankenstein*. Monstrous Mary was only 18 when she dreamed up this story of a man put together like a Lego kit. Seriously weird writer.

7. Wilson was sentenced to be hanged, drawn and quartered. In fact he was hanged then beheaded. His 'crime' was to lead a march in protest against unemployment.

8. A pumpkin. She probably changed it each time she rode, which is more than she did with her stockings. She wore them till they stank.

9. Tights. He had them made the colour of his flesh because he didn't want to look like a wimp.

10. Rugby. He picked up the ball and ran with it. The game was named after his public school, Rugby, so we don't say, 'Fancy a game of Ellis?'

11. He sold them to doctors so they could experiment on them. Of course the doctors weren't punished.

12. Huskisson stepped from his carriage to say hello to friends, was hit by a train and died.

13. The disease of cholera. Not only does it give you disgusting diarrhoea but victims turn blue before they die. 20,000 died in the next year.

14. Women (and boys under 10) were no longer allowed to work in mines. They lost their wages so it isn't all good news.

15. It was a sign of bad weather on the way. People were glad of the warning. Modern weather forecasts smell better.

16. 'The train's so slow, I was 12 when I got on it.' On most lines 30 mph was thought to be quite fast enough.

17. They were looking for coins and metal dropped through drains. Would you stick your hand down a toilet for your pocket money? Toshers would.

18. They were emigrating from Ireland because they were starving in the potato famine. The old ships, nicknamed coffin ships, didn't always make it. Starve or drown? Some choice.

19. It rained heavily and many people stayed at home rather than get wet.

20. It was the first flushing public toilet for men – but not women, who would have to keep their legs crossed!

21. Convicts. Australia was a dumping ground for Brit criminals and now it stopped. Brit criminals got harsher sentences at home instead and no kangaroo steaks.

22. They were dumped outside the hospital and eaten by pigs. Then the pigs were eaten by the patients ... including the patients who lost arms and legs. You could say they ended up eating themselves! Yeuch!

23. Soccer. The new rules said that only the goalkeeper could handle the ball. It also banned fighting on the pitch. Someone should tell today's players!

24. Canada! Yes it sounds odd but with the help of US troops the Irish rebels attacked Brit troops in Canada as the first stage of attacking Brit troops in Ireland.

25. Moustaches. Sailors could be clean shaven or wear beards, but moustaches were popular with soldiers and the navy didn't want its men to look like their great rivals in the army!

26. Charles Dickens. He was only 58 but was racing around the country, reading and acting his characters. It killed him.

27. Go to school. The Education Reform Act forced everyone to suffer at school whether they liked it or not.

28. 'Yes.' Not very chatty when someone had come all that way to interview him, was it?

29. None. The inspector wasn't trained and had never inspected a bridge before. He wouldn't have known a bad bridge if it had jumped up and bitten him on the nose.

30. George Eliot was a woman, real name Mary Anne Evans. She didn't think publishers would

print a book by a woman so she lied and said she was a man.

31. The ship slid into the river, rolled over and drowned 124 of them. Well, they built it, so they couldn't complain – and they didn't.

32. A Bible. Very cool. Unfortunately the Bible was no defence against the spear that killed him.

33. Jack the Ripper. He killed eight women and the mystery has never been forgotten – or solved. But Queen Victoria showed an unusual interest in the case. Hmmmm!

34. An elephant. Joseph Merrick was known as the Elephant Man and he was treated as a freak, rather than a sick person. He died aged just 27.

35. Smaller. Blackpool Tower is only half the height of the Eiffel Tower – but people falling off the top end up with exactly the same amount of deadness.

36. The kangaroos were in the first cinema show in Britain. Now you know the answer you'll be hoppy.

37. Motorists were now allowed to drive without being led by a man with a red flag. The speed limit also went up from 4 mph to 20 mph. Scary!

38. An early hang glider.

39. Glass eyes. His favourite was a bloodshot eye which he used when he had a cold!

40. Tins of chocolate.

Question of the century

41. They both have 'the' as their middle name! Boring answer: William the Fourth was a sailor, and so was Popeye.

Umms and Errs

42. Mother. 'On the telephone' is definitely wrong! So is 'a taxi'.

43. Die. 'Fight and win' would not be very English – look at the present-day cricket team.

44. Pity. 'Bury' makes a bit more sense, you have to admit.

45. Unhand. Not a word you'll hear very often but remember it next time a history teacher grabs you!

46. Polish. This is such a famous line your granny probably knows it. In fact she probably ate the pies!

47. Love. 'Get chocolates from' is not a good enough answer.

Behave like a Victorian

48. Don't. Wait until they have offered it to you.

49. Do. And remember you mustn't gurgle or suck in your breath while you sip your soup.

50. Don't. Write letters or nothing at all.

51. Do. Even if it's only a very short call.

52. Don't. Well, usually. There are some slang words that a gentleman may use. If you don't know what they are then avoid slang altogether.

53. Don't. Break off a piece and place it in your mouth.

54. Don't. Call them maids or servants.

55. Do. BUT ... wait till she has bowed to you first and do not wave your hat in the air the way the French do – put it straight back on to your head.

56. Don't. Or anywhere else for that matter!

57. Don't. The book admits that most men do this but says it is extremely impolite.

Manchester misery

58. c) In London slums people would, on average, live 22 years – but average upper class people would live twice as long. The unhealthiest place to live in 1842 was Liverpool, where the average age of death was just 15 years old. Queen Victoria lived to be 81. The average age was so low because lots of children died very young.

Trasseno talk

59. No. A 'chat' was a louse that crawls around your body. Are you sure you fancy one?

60. No. To 'nail' something is to 'steal' it. Doors were popular for sleeping on. Propped up on a few bricks, a door would keep you off the damp floor – unfortunately it wasn't high enough to keep the rats off you.

61. Yes. Well, maybe. . . A 'finny' was a five pound note, but be careful because a Trasseno might try to give you some 'flash' money – a worthless imitation. The forgers didn't try to copy money – that was a serious offence and you could be hanged for it until 1832. Instead they made notes that looked like money, but with the 'Bank of Engraving' written on them instead of the

'Bank of England'.

62. No. A 'dewskitch' was a beating – usually with a strap, a birch (a bundle of twigs) or a cane.

63. No. 'Flummut' meant dangerous.

64. No. A 'jack' was Trasseno language for a policeman. Of course policemen were also called 'Bobbies' or 'Peelers' because they were organized by Sir Robert Peel.

65. No. A 'flat' person wasn't someone who's been squashed by a flummut horse! It was someone who is easily tricked ... and you wouldn't admit that!

66. No. 'Nammo' should really be spelled 'namow' because it meant 'woman' (spelled backwards). Most back-slang words have slipped out of use – we no longer say 'yennap' for a penny and no one drinks 'reeb' any more. But you might still be a 'yob'!

67. No. A 'jolly' person was one who starts a fight in public! They could be useful; they'd start a fight and get everyone's attention so that the fine-wirers, flimps and gonophs (pick-pockets) could go to work stealing unguarded purses.

68. Yes. Well, you should... 'Flag' means apron.

Odd one out

69. Hot air balloon – OUT. First flight made in 1783 near Paris.

70. Aeroplane – OUT. Orville Wright made the first powered heavier-than air flight in 1903.

71. Parachute – OUT because the first jump was made from a hot-air balloon in 1797. You can be excused for getting this one wrong because the first jump in Britain was in 1802 and the first jump by a British person (who lived) was in 1838. The year before a Brit died trying.

72. Multi-storey car park – OUT . . . but only just. In May 1901 an electric carriage company built a 7-storey garage for its vehicles.

73. Telephone – IN-vented 1876. US inventor Alexander Graham Bell usually gets the credit for this. (Although Johann Reis of Germany did show a telephone device in 1860 made of a violin case and a sausage skin!)

74. Box kite – IN-vented in Australia, 1893.

75. Photographic camera – IN-vented in the 1820s and 30s.

76. Railway signal box – IN-vented in London 1839.

77. Railway station – IN-vented in Baltimore, USA, in 1830.

78. Policeman – OUT. The London police force was created in 1829 but the world's first was in Paris 1667.

79. Motor car – IN-vented in France in 1862. The 19th century also saw the first road death (London 1896), drunken driver (London 1897), car theft (Paris 1896) and speeding motorist (Kent 1896).

80. Railway locomotive – IN-vented in 1804 by Richard Trevithick. The Victorian age was the age of the railways with steam trains crossing the country. The first railway death was in 1828, when driver John Gillespie's boiler blew up on the famous Stockton and Darlington railway.

81. Pedal cycle – IN-vented in Scotland in 1839.

82. Football goal nets. IN-vented by a Liverpool engineer in 1890.

83. Women footballers – IN-vented in 1895 by Lady Florence Dixie who formed the British Women's Football Club.

Name that kid

84–93. All are true – except 87 and 89.

Howzat Victoria

94. She was the shortest in height but the longest in the time she spent on the throne.

95. The dirty water from her toilet leaked into Albert's drinking water and gave him the disease that killed him.

96. The gunman tried to shoot her as she drove in her carriage in London. His gun misfired and he escaped. The police told her to drive in the same place and at the same time the next day so that he could try again. He did! They caught him.

97. She was buried with a photograph of her 'friend', her Scottish servant. In her hand was a lock of his hair. What had they been up to when she was alive, people wanted to know!

98. Victoria proposed to him!

99. Victoria (and hubby Albert) preferred the people in the pictures to have no clothes on!

100. She was from the German Hanover family so she always spoke with a German accent.

The 1900s
The 20th Century

This was the age of war – followed by more war. An age when new machines meant people could kill in new ways, kill more and kill faster. History hasn't changed much; it's simply gone from horrible to horribler.

Quick questions

1. In 1901 old Queen Victoria died and was popped into her coffin. The family lined up to see her. How did they show their respect? (Clue: x)

2. In 1902 the British police had a new way of detecting some crimes. What? (Clue: criminals went hand in glove with this idea)

3. In 1909 the police had yet another exciting new weapon! A vehicle for chasing criminals. What? (Clue: spokesmen?)

4. Scott of the Antarctic set off on his 1910 expedition sponsored by Oxo. They proudly produced a poster showing a polar bear but had to scrap it. Why? (Clue: the new posters showed penguins instead)

5. Scott wasn't the only one who failed to come back. So did 1,500 people whose jolly journey ended disastrously in 1912. What happened to them? (Clue: it was unthinkable?)

6. 1912 was a year for disasters. A man jumped off the Eiffel Tower, expecting to live, but died. What was he trying to do? (Clue: not opening time)

7. In 1913 a suffragette, fighting to get votes for women, jumped in front of a horse at the Derby to get publicity. Who owned the horse? (Clue: she was thrown to the ground, he was just throned)

8. In August 1914 the First World War started. What did Brit soldiers wear to protect their heads? (Clue: they were flat)

9. The war ended in 1918 with almost 9 million dead. But by 1919 another 20 million had died! What disaster was greater than the war? (Clue: it flew round the world)

10. Lord Caernarvon found his lost

mummy in 1922. Where? (Clue: wrapped up safely)

11. In 1926 the General Strike meant Britain needed lots of Special Police to control the strikers. Why did the Special Police need chair legs? (Clue: it's a cracking idea)

12. In 1928 there was a curious craze for racing a particular type of horse. What? (Clue: rock and roll?)

13. In 1930 the great airship R101 set off on a flight. The makers could have used explosive gas or safe gas. They used explosive gas – and it exploded. Why did they choose that gas? (Clue: sounds like a budgie?)

14. In the hard-up 1930s an unemployed vicar made money by starving himself while people paid to watch. He took his performance into a lion's cage. How did the lion entertain the crowds? (Clue: vicar and lion are no longer starving)

15. When the Second World War started in 1939 civilians were urged to join the Local Defence Volunteers. Comedians said LDV stood for Look, Duck and . . . what? (Clue: Vanquish? Not quite.)

16. In May 1940 Mr Hitler did something a certain Mr Fawkes failed to do. What? (Clue: remember?)

17. In 1940 a man was arrested for

lighting a cigarette. Why? (Clue: night-light)

18. The British government tried to ban Londoners sheltering in the Underground stations during bombing raids. What did the crafty Cockneys do? (Clue: train for it)

19. Car headlights were masked because of the blackout. How did farmers protect their black cattle that may have strayed on to the road? (Clue: zebra crossing?)

20. Why did parents have to label every piece of their children's clothing during the war? (Clue: bits and pieces)

21. During the war, the tops of pillar-boxes were painted green or yellow. Why? (Clue: it's a gas)

22. When the war ended in 1945 some children tried to eat bananas without peeling them. Why? (Clue: Yes! We have no bananas!)

23. In 1949 the Wimbledon tennis star Gussie Moran shocked the world with a sight of what? (Clue: it would have been more shocking if they hadn't been there!)

24. In 1953 Queen Elizabeth II was crowned and the coronation was shown on television at the new queen's insistance. Why? (Clue: for granny's sake)

25. In 1957 the first US astronauts were two monkeys. They were wired up for tests. The monkeys returned safely but what happened to one monkey as the wires were removed? (Clue: no more monkeying around)

26. In 1960 Britain invented a terror that became known as 'The Yellow Peril'. What is the Yellow peril? (Clue: they go where yellow lines go)

27. In 1963 there was a sensational crime. What is it known as? (Clue: the villains did NOT steal the huge trailing bit of a wedding dress)

28. In 1969 Egyptian radio called it 'The greatest human achievement ever.' What? (Clue: the Americans made it and it isn't a beefburger)

29. In the 1960s the Americans went one better and created the Funky Chicken. What was it? (Clue: beat it not eat it)

30. In 1974 a Japanese soldier stepped out of a Philippine jungle and surrendered. What had he done? (Clue: living in the past)

31. In 1977 he died on the toilet. Even today people say the death was a fake and that they've seen him. What was this man's career when he was alive? (Clue: lemonade warbler?)

32. In 1979 the British Prime Minister was seen carrying a handbag. Whose handbag? (Clue: not the queen mother's)

33. Britain went to war again in 1982. 99% of Brits said 'We are fighting *where*?'

So? Where? (Clue: sheep and penguins know the answer!)

34. In 1984 animal rights protestors were furious with bags of crisps. Why? (Clue: they weren't to the taste of these prickly people)

35. In 1987 a BBC weather forecaster said it was NOT going to happen – then it did. What? (Clue: it was a blow to his reputation)

36. They rioted in England in 1381 and they rioted again for the same reason in 1990. Why? (Clue: sounds like sharp little carpet nails for a Polish person)

37. War again! This time Brits and allies defeated the Iraqi forces who had taken over the oil fields of Kuwait. The Iraqis were bad losers. What did they do as they retreated? (Clue: oil get you in the end!)

38. In 1993 a Brit explorer failed to reach the South Pole, just like Scott of the Antarctic eighty years before. But he survived. How? (Clue: Scott didn't have one)

39. In 1994 Elizabeth became the first Brit monarch to go directly to France without going over the English Channel. How did she manage this miracle? (Clue: it was a great under-taking)

40. In the 1990s the plague was a distant memory but people gave up eating beef because of a new fear. What? (Clue: is this the sane thing to do?)

Awful agents

In the years before the First World War, there were a lot of German spies in Britain because they guessed that war was on its way. Some of the German spies were not too clever. In fact they were awful agents. The simple spymen selected the titles of popular songs to match the secret word. So, you might say 'All I need is the air that I breathe' to mean 'airport'. Can you match the real meaning to the code word?

41. Submarines
a) Floating down
b) Don't sink twice, it's alright
c) Don't you make my drowned eyes blue

42. Old battleships
a) Old folks at home
b) We are the champions
c) Sailing

43. Dartmouth Naval Base
a) Dark melodies
b) Don't go breaking my dart
c) I left my dart in San Francisco

44. Chatham Base
a) Chattanooga Rag
b) Chat me up before you go-go
c) Chat'll be the day

45. Southampton
a) Down South
b) South of the border
c) It's a long way to tip a fairy

46. Destroyers
a) Pirates of Penzance
b) Rule Britannia
c) Land of dope and gory

That'll teach 'em

In the dark and terrible days of the 20th century (before 1986), suffering schoolchildren could have their legs slapped or their knuckles rapped with a ruler. But the most painful punishment of all was the cane – usually a thin bamboo rod smacked across your hand or your backside.

We know about some of the terrible crimes punished by the cane from a 1920s 'punishment book' from a Birmingham girls' school. Which of the following were caning offences?

47. Talking in class.
48. A sarcastic expression.
49. Lateness.
50. Smiling.
51. Laziness.

52. Sucking a boiled sweet.
53. Writing in the lavatory.
54. Deliberately disobeying a teacher.
55. Not being very clever.
56. Losing a book.

Second World War wonders

Try this quick quiz on the Second World War. Replace the words '*Laurel and Hardy*' with one of the answers below. One of those answers *is* '*Laurel and Hardy*'!

57. British and Allied troops coloured everything khaki brown as camouflage. They even had khaki *Laurel and Hardy*.

58. The British Home Guard were warned that an enemy paratrooper might be disguised as *Laurel and Hardy*.

59. Some spies in Germany were executed by *Laurel and Hardy*.

60. British soldiers in Italy were given summer *Laurel and Hardy* and some died of the cold.

61. In November 1940 a man called Lloyd was arrested in Britain for having *Laurel and Hardy* in his back garden.

62. US paratroopers were safer than British ones because they had two *Laurel and Hardy*.

63. The Germans sent *Laurel and Hardy* into battle when they became short of soldiers.

64. The Nazis thought ideal *Laurel and Hardy* should have broad hips.

65. Workers who were late for work in a German factory ended up in *Laurel and Hardy*.

66. Italian leader Mussolini was said to look like one half of *Laurel and Hardy*.

WELL THIS WAR IS CERTAINLY KEEPING US BUSY OLLIE!

The missing words are: uniforms, 16-year-old boys, Laurel and Hardy, bonfires, nuns, toilet rolls, women, prison, parachutes, guillotines.

Question of the century

67. In the Second World War, how often did parachutes fail to open?

Sixties swingers

Your parents might be old enough to remember the 1960s. If so, they'll tell you that the music of that time was the best ever. But will they be able to answer these 60s music questions? Pester your parent (or grab your granny and ask her) – they have to answer true or false. . .

68. One of Marvin Gaye's classic hits was *The World is Like a Great Big Onion*.

69. At the end of the Beatles song *Strawberry Fields Forever*, John Lennon can be heard muttering 'Apple sauce, apple sauce, apple sauce,' as the music fades.

70. The lyrics of the Byrds hit song *Turn! Turn! Turn!* were written by a king of ancient Israel around 950 BC.

71. The Who used to spray their audiences with champagne at their gigs.

72. Singer Dave Berry, who had a sixties hit with *The Crying Game*, told his audience he would be reincarnated as a snake.

20th century teasers

Test a teacher with these questions on the last century of the massive millennium.

73. Which of these predictions for the end of the millennium was made in 1985?
a) petrol engines would be a thing of the past
b) starvation would no longer exist
c) everyone in Britain would need specs from watching too much TV

74. In 1961, the Russians sent the first human, Yuri Gagarin, into space. But four years earlier they had sent their first astronaut, who was a. . .
a) monkey
b) dog
c) tortoise

75. In 1949 the Simplified Spelling Society almost succeeded in changing the way we spell in Britain. Their ideas were put to Parliament but were rejected by 87 votes to 84. What was their book called?
a) New Spelling
b) Nue Spelling
c) Nou Spellin

76. How much did the first pocket calculators cost to buy in the UK? (They first became available in 1972.)
a) £12.50
b) £79
c) £7.99

77. In the 1940s you could eat 'chicken fruit on bacon ducks'. What was it?
a) boiled beef and carrots
b) omelette with sun dried tomatoes
c) eggs on fried bread

78. In 1982 Queen Elizabeth II was the victim of a crime. What was it?
a) she was mugged during a 'walkabout'
b) she woke up in the night to find an intruder sitting on the end of her bed
c) someone dog-napped her corgis

79. During the Second World War, US soldiers were advised to eat. . .
a) caterpillars
b) maggots
c) absolutely anything

80. In the Falkland Islands war in 1982, the average age of the British soldiers was...
a) 19
b) 22
c) 24

Out of time

The twentieth century has been a great hundred years for inventions. Here are 14 important twentieth century things. But how many were first made in the last hundred years?

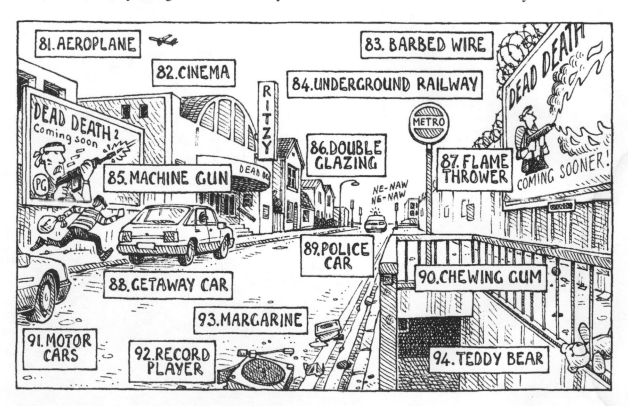

War-like words?

At the end of the millennium, people are still bombing and killing but they've found some new words to describe it so that they *sound* less horrible. See if you can work out what these military phrases mean.

Words	Meaning
95. air support	**a)** human beings
96. friendly fire	**b)** destroy
97. neutralizing	**c)** planes dropping bombs
98. soft targets	**d)** blowing people to pieces by mistake
99. collateral damage	**e)** assassinating a human nuisance
100. immobilize	**f)** shooting soldiers on your own side

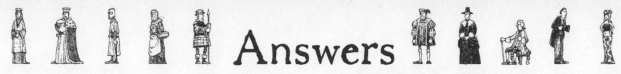

Answers

Quick questions

1. They kissed the corpse's hand.
2. Fingerprints. The idea had been around for 20 years but the first conviction in Britain came in 1902. The villainous Harry Jackson was convicted of the dreadful crime of stealing . . . billiard balls!
3. Bicycles.
4. Polar bears live at the North pole – the Arctic – not the South Pole. And Scott of the Antarctic was going to the Antarctic ... but he didn't come back.
5. They were on the RMS *Titanic* when it hit an iceberg.
6. He was testing a parachute.
7. The king, George V.
8. Caps. Steel helmets weren't used for another year and by then a lot of heads had stopped a lot of shrapnel.
9. Spanish flu . . . though it probably started in America!
10. In an Egyptian tomb. The mummy he discovered was that of Tutankhamun.
11. To hit people with. The police force had run out of truncheons.
12. Rocking-horse races. Especially popular among adults with rocking-horse brains.
13. It was cheap. Deadly – but cheap. Of course it put people off airship travel.
14. The lion ate the vicar.
15. Vanish. The LDV went on to become the Home Guard, popularly known as 'Dad's Army'.
16. His bombs flattened the Houses of Parliament.
17. He was breaking the blackout laws in force during the war.
18. They bought platform tickets so no one could stop them going down to safety.
19. They painted white stripes down their sides.
20. If the child was blown to pieces then the bits could be identified. Gruesome but true-some.
21. So that droplets of deadly mustard gas would stain the paint and show if there was a gas attack.
22. Many children had never seen a banana and didn't know what to do with it.
23. Her frilly knickers.
24. Elizabeth's granny was sick and couldn't get to the ceremony. The queen wanted her to be able to watch on television.

25. The monkey died.
26. The Yellow Perils are traffic wardens. Rumours are still going around that Adolf Hitler survived the war and became a traffic warden. This may not be true.
27. The Great Train Robbery, when a mail train was robbed of sacks full of wrinkly old money on its way to be burned. Seemed a shame to waste it, the robbers thought.
28. The Americans landed on the moon. This was one small step for man. As usual women were left behind.
29. It was a dance. So was the Twist and doctors warned young people against it in case they sprained their ankles. The doctors clearly had sprained brains.
30. He had fought in the Second World War. He didn't know that it had ended 29 years before.
31. Pop singer, Elvis Presley. Fans tried to snatch his body before it was buried. Maybe (like Oliver Cromwell) the corpse was replaced by a dummy! History repeats itself, they say.
32. Her own handbag. Margaret Thatcher had become the first woman Prime Minister.
33. The Falkland Islands in the South Atlantic. Argentina believed these cold, wet, sheep-infested rocks belonged to them. Brits and Argies fought and died for them.
34. A pub was offering hedgehog flavoured crisps. It was a joke. Sadly some people have no sense of humour.
35. A hurricane hit southern England.
36. The rioters didn't want to pay their Poll Tax.
37. They set fire to the oil wells and caused huge pollution problems. Smoking is very bad for the Earth's health.
38. He was collected by a helicopter. Takes a bit of the sport out of it, doesn't it?
39. She went under – in the newly opened Channel Tunnel.
40. Mad cow disease. Why were the cows mad? Well, probably because the farmers were pinching all their milk.

Awful agents

41–46. All the answers are a). Difficult, eh?

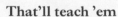

That'll teach 'em

47–56. All of them were punished with the cane except 48, 52 and 55.

Second World War wonders

57. Toilet rolls. A quick flash of white could give them away to the enemy!

58. Nuns. Or vicars or a woman carrying a baby.

59. Guillotines. In August 1942 German spy-catchers uncovered a team of 46 spies. The male spies were hanged, but for some reason the female spies were guillotined.

60. Uniforms. The army planners believed it would be very hot in Italy, but it was wet and cold and in the mountains it was freezing.

61. Bonfires. Mr Lloyd supported the Nazi party. The magistrate gave Lloyd a prison sentence – Lloyd gave the magistrate a Nazi salute.

62. Parachutes. The British Army said two parachutes took up too much room. The truth was probably that it would have been too expensive.

63. 16-year-old boys. As the war went on and the fit men were killed or captured the German Army called for older men and younger boys to join.

64. Women. The ideal Nazi woman should also have blonde hair, never wear make-up or trousers, and wear her hair in a bun or plaits.

65. Prison. You could be sentenced to three months in prison. (And you thought an hour's detention for being late to school was cruel!)

66. Laurel and Hardy. Mussolini was short and fat. When he became ruler of Italy he wore a dark suit and a bowler hat. Somebody told him he looked just like Oliver Hardy – a comic idiot – so he began dressing in military uniforms instead.

Question of the century

67. Only once!

Sixties swingers

68. True.

69. False. John Lennon actually says, 'Cranberry sauce, cranberry sauce, cranberry sauce'!

70. True. The band adapted the lyrics from a section of the Bible written by King Solomon.

71. False. But audiences might have been sprayed with spit, because the band would spit at and fight one another at gigs.

72. True. He used to twine himself around his microphone stand!

20th century teasers

73.a) The inventor of the electric tricycle predicted this.

74.b) She was called Laika.

75.b)

76.b)

77.c)

78.b)

79.b) A US Army handbook advised them to eat maggots and grasshoppers (with the wings and legs removed!), but advised against eating caterpillars.

80.a)

Out of time

81. Aeroplane – Yes. First powered heavier-than-air flight in USA, 1903.

82. Cinema – No. New Orleans 1896.

83. Barbed wire – No. 1867

84. Underground railway – No. 1870.

85. Machine gun – No. First used in war in 1879.

86. Double glazing – No. England, 1874.

87. Flame-thrower – Yes. Gas-powered machine invented in Berlin, 1900.

88. Getaway car – Yes. Three Paris shop-robbers used one in 1901.

89. Police car – Yes. USA, 1903. (Two years after the first criminals used a car! A bit late!)

90. Chewing gum – No. 1872.

91. Motor cars – No. First petrol car 1883

92. Record player – No. 1879.

93. Margarine – No. 1869.

94. Teddy Bear – Yes. 1902 but the USA and Germany still argue over who had the first teddy.

War-like words

95.c) 96.f) 97.e) 98.a) 99.d) 100.b)